DUQUESNE STUDIES
Philosophical Series

19

EVOLUTION AND PHILOSOPHY

DUQUESNE STUDIES
Philosophical Series

19

EVOLUTION AND PHILOSOPHY

by

ANDREW G. VAN MELSEN

DUQUESNE UNIVERSITY PRESS
Pittsburgh, Pa.
Editions E. NAUWELAERTS, LOUVAIN
1965

Library of Congress Catalog Card Number 65-25666

All rights reserved
© 1965, by Duquesne University
Printed in the United States of America by
The Ad Press, Ltd., New York, N. Y.

DUQUESNE STUDIES

Philosophical Series

Andrew G. van Melsen, D.Sc., D.Ed., and Henry J. Koren, C.S.Sp. S.T.D., editors.

Volume One—*Andrew G. van Melsen,* FROM ATOMOS TO ATOM. Out of print. Available in Torchbook edition from Harper Brothers. Published also in Dutch, German, Spanish and Italian.

Volume Two—*Andrew G. van Melsen,* THE PHILOSOPHY OF NATURE. Pp. XII and 265. Third edition, fourth impression. Price: paper $3.75, cloth $4.50. Published also in Italian, Dutch and Polish editions.

Volume Three—*P. Henry van Laer,* PHILOSOPHICO-SCIENTIFIC PROBLEMS. Out of print.

Volume Four—*Cajetan's,* THE ANALOGY OF NAMES AND THE CONCEPT OF BEING. Pp. X and 93. Second Edition. Price: $2.25, cloth.

Volume Five—*Louis de Raeymaeker and others,* TRUTH AND FREEDOM. Pp. VII and 132. Second impression. Price: $3.00 cloth. Published also in French.

Volume Six—*P. Henry van Laer,* THE PHILOSOPHY OF SCIENCE. PART ONE: SCIENCE IN GENERAL. Pp. XVII and 164. Second edition. Price: cloth $3.75

Volume Seven—*Stephen Strasser,* THE SOUL IN METAPHYSICAL AND EMPIRICAL PSYCHOLOGY. Pp. X and 275. Second impression. Price: cloth $6.00. Published also in German, Dutch and French.

Volume Eight—*Albert Dondeyne,* CONTEMPORARY EUROPEAN THOUGHT AND CHRISTIAN FAITH. Pp. XI and 211. Second impression. Price: paper $5.00, cloth $5.75. Published also in French.

Volume Nine—*Maxwell J. Charlesworth,* PHILOSOPHY AND LINGUISTIC ANALYSIS. Pp. XIII and 234. Second impression. Price: paper $4.75, cloth $5.50.

Volume Ten—*Remy C. Kwant,* PHILOSOPHY OF LABOR. Pp. XI and 163. Price: paper $4.50, cloth $5.25.

Volume Eleven—*Remy C. Kwant,* ENCOUNTER. Pp. VIII and 85. Second impression. Price: cloth $3.25. Published also in Dutch.

Volume Twelve—*William A. Luijpen*, EXISTENTIAL PHENOME-
NOLOGY. Pp. XIII and 355. Fourth impression. Price: cloth $6.25.
Published also in Dutch.

Volume Thirteen—*Andrew G. van Melsen*, SCIENCE AND TECH-
NOLOGY. Pp. X and 373. Price: paper $6.20, cloth $6.95. Published also in Dutch and German.

Volume Fourteen—*P. Henry van Laer*, PHILOSOPHY OF SCIENCE.
Part Two: A Study of the Division and Nature of Various Groups
of Sciences. Pp. XIII and 342. Price: paper $5.75, cloth, $6.50.

Volume Fifteen—*Remy C. Kwant*, THE PHENOMENOLOGICAL PHI-
LOSOPHY OF MERLEAU-PONTY. Pp. IX and 257. Price: cloth $5.25.

Volume Sixteen—*John A. Peters*, METAPHYSICS: A SYSTEMATIC
SURVEY. Pp. XVIII and 529. Price: paper $9.00, cloth $9.75.

Volume Seventeen—*William A. Luijpen*, PHENOMENOLOGY AND
ATHEISM. Pp. XIV and 343. Price: paper $5.75, cloth $6.50.

Volume Eighteen—*Martin G. Plattel*, SOCIAL PHILOSOPHY. Pp. XI
and 345. Price: paper $7.20, cloth $7.95. Published also in Dutch
and German.

Volume Nineteen—*Andrew G. van Melsen*, EVOLUTION AND PHI-
LOSOPHY. Pp. 208. Price: paper $4.75, cloth $5.50.

IN PREPARATION:

Joseph A. Kockelmans, *Phenomenology and Physical Science*

DUQUESNE STUDIES are published in the following series: African,
Philological, Philosophical, Psychological, Spiritan and Theological.

Periodical publications of Duquesne University Press:

Annuale Mediaevale ($4.00 per year); Duquesne Hispanic Re-
view ($3.00 per year); Duquesne Review. A Journal of the Social
Sciences ($2.25 per year); Duquesne Science Counselor ($3.00
per year; $3.25 outside U.S.); Journal of Ecumenical Studies
($6.00 per year); Review of Existential Psychology and Psy-
chiatry ($5.00 per year); Humanitas ($5.00 per year); Envoy
(a Religion and Personality Newsletter—$3.00 per year).

CONTENTS

PREFACE

This book contains many ideas concerning evolution, the importance of physical science, the relationship between physical science and philosophy, matter, life, causality and finality about which the author has previously written in other works. Nevertheless, the idea of gathering those scattered materials together in book form and thereby making them more easily accessible has not been the main reason for this publication. Otherwise the author could have restricted himself to a simple reproduction of those articles and essays, accompanied by the necessary adaptations and corrections. The idea of writing this work arose from the conviction that in the previously published materials on those topics there was a leading idea which nowhere managed to develop its full potential and which perhaps the author himself did not yet clearly visualize. For this reason *Evolution and Philosophy* has become a new book, with respect to which the previously published articles play the role of preparatory studies and sources of reference.

Andrew G. van Melsen

The American edition of this book does not differ from the original edition, except for the omission of a few references to Dutch books and articles, the substitution of corresponding English works, and some very slight modifications in the text. The translation was made by the undersigned from the author's manuscript and submitted to him for his personal approval.

Duquesne University   Henry J. Koren, C.S.Sp.

INTRODUCTION

The concept "evolution" is one of the concepts illustrating that specialization remains something relative in science. In almost every science the concept "evolution," in one form or in another, plays an important role. It is difficult to determine where the idea to conceive reality as not static but dynamic first became firmly planted in man's mind. The view which regards reality as developing is very old. It existed in many mythologies as well as in ancient Greek thought.[1]

There is a difference, however, between the origin of an idea and the period in which this idea becomes a generally accepted and useful category of scientific thought. If this difference is kept in mind, thinking in terms of development, progress and evolution undoubtedly originated in the new era after the rise of physical science. This statement should not be understood as if the specific meaning attached to the term "evolution" in biology is its oldest and most central sense. It was only in the course of the nineteenth century that the idea of evolution in the biological sense acquired a crucial importance in biology itself, but a century before that man was already largely dominated by his belief in progress. For this reason we may not exclude that the idea of progress and especially the realization that man is an historical being have indirectly influenced the origin of the biological theory of evolution.[2]

On the other hand, it is certain that the biological theory of evolution has greatly stimulated thinking along evolutionary lines in other sciences. It is quite common now to refer to evolution in law, language, arts, morals and customs, social conditions and even in dogmatic theology. This commonly accepted way of speaking bears witness to the stimulating influence exercised by the biological theory of evolution.

It is true, of course, that the term "evolution" does not always have the same meaning. Yet it always implies the idea of a change in the sense of a more or less continuous development of something which originally existed only in capacity. Evolution, however, does

---

[1]Cf. W. Zimmermann, *Evolution, die Geschichte ihrer Probleme und Erkenntnisse,* Freiburg, 2nd ed., 1954, pp. 1-77.

[2]Concerning this problem, see K. Kuypers, "Het evolutiebegrip en zijn toepassing op de mens," *De evolutieleer na honderd jaar,* Haarlem, 1959.

not necessarily refer to a development that is to be evaluated as progress, as development toward something higher or better. "Evolution" and "progress" therefore are not at all interchangeable terms. The later development is not *per se* the better. There is, moreover, the problem of how to find a norm by which evolution in a particular field can be evaluated as progress. This problem is not too difficult with respect to development in science, the evolution of man's scientific thinking. No one doubts that the development of physical science since the seventeenth century is real progress, but can we speak of progress in art? Or to remain closer to professional interest, what are we to say about the development of philosophy? Is there question here of progress or merely of diversification, of development in many directions? Regardless of the reply to this question, if philosophy undergoes a development that can be called "progress," there is no doubt at all that the form assumed by its progress differs from that of physical science.

Similar problems arise when we want to speak about the evolution of society. Undoubtedly, this evolution contains aspects with respect to which there is every reason to speak of progress, but can one speak here of progress also along the entire line of society's development? The question becomes particularly painful if we ask whether man as man has really made progress in all his scientific, cultural and social developments. Is there, for example, progress in morality?

Even within the realm considered by biology evolution may not simply be identified with progress. Undoubtedly, there is reason to call the evolution from the non-living to the living and from there to man "progress." Nevertheless, concentrating all attention on this aspect of the total picture of evolution, as it is studied by the biologist, gives a lopsided idea of this picture. Even in the realm of the living, evolution points to diversification as much as to progress.

Although evolution and progress may not be simply identified, it remains meaningful to connect these two ideas. This meaningfulness manifests itself most clearly when there is question of evolutions accomplished and pursued by man. The above-mentioned example of the pursuit of science is particularly eloquent in this matter. In his scientific pursuits man deliberately tends to know more and to know better, so that the direction of development is predelineated. The same may be said with respect to man's technical development and certain aspects of society's evolution, for here also there are deliberately pursued aims.

Strange as it may seem, however, the results of these pursuits often differ considerably from man's expectations. Certain developments wanted and pursued by him appear to have repercussions that go far beyond man's original intentions. This phenomenon is connected with the fact that man's knowledge and power are only partial. He grasps only certain aspects and never the totality of reality. This fact raises a peculiar problem, viz., to what extent the developmental processes started by man possess a kind of autonomy in the way in which they run their course. Frequently these developments strongly suggest that man's deliberate aims hardly retain control over their course. Man sometimes feels himself the executor of a program of development rather than its originator. Accordingly, it seems that the criterion to decide whether or not there is question of progress does not at all depend solely on man's deliberate and purposive action. The matter is more complex than this.

This problem is important especially because it throws some light on the question whether one can correctly use one and the same term, "evolution," in distinct sciences. At first sight it would seem reasonable to assume that evolution in a realm of human reality, e.g., that of science, is totally different from evolution in the material cosmos or in the realms of plants and animals. Man's purposive development of culture should not be placed on a par with the evolutionary causes, whatever they be, of plants and animals. It seems to be an unfortunate use of terms, therefore, to speak in both cases of "evolution," for this way of speaking suggests an equality that is not really present.

On the other hand, however, the phenomenon that the development of technology and its influence upon the social order obey a kind of inner necessity points to the fact that, in many respects, the difference between cosmic, biological, and cultural developments is not as large as it seems to be at first. To some extent their similarity is not too difficult to understand if one takes man's nature into account. For in all his cultural achievements man has to make use of material means. This fact makes it reasonable to expect certain fundamental characteristics of material evolution to manifest themselves also in all other developments. From this it follows that physical science, whose task it is to study matter and its possible evolutions, retains special importance with respect to man's development in all kinds of realms.

The preceding considerations indicate more or less the chief topic of this book, which is to investigate whether physical science occupies a key-position in any kind of evolution pursued by man. This idea appears very attractive if we keep the following in mind. According to the theory of evolution, man has evolved from the evolution occurring in material reality, which was governed directly by natural causes. On the other hand, evolution which is brought about by man himself would have its basis in man's science of nature, that is, in his purposive manipulation of the known possibilities of nature. However, attractive as the idea may be, it does not mean that it is also true. It has to be investigated very carefully.

To eliminate at once a possible misunderstanding, we must add that the hypothesis that physical science occupies perhaps a key-position does not imply that this kind of science is the only legitimate form of science. But it does imply that the development of physical science somehow is the condition for the development of other forms of science and also of the social evolution that is guided by these other forms of science. In particular, the hypothesis implies that the development of physical science is of essential importance for the development of philosophy. For this reason the title given to this book is *Evolution and Philosophy*.

The use of this title does not mean that the purpose of this book is limited to a philosophical reflection upon the problems raised by the biological theory of evolution. Although that reflection constitutes a large part of this work, it serves a wider purpose, viz., to investigate what possible consequences follow from the evolutionary problematics with respect to developments that are purposively pursued and accomplished by man himself. This investigation will be limited mainly to a disclosure of the key-position occupied by physcal science in these developments. Moreover, we will not consider the importance of physical science for the evolution of technology and society, for these topics have been treated in our book *Science and Technology* (Vol. 13 of Duquesne Studies, *Philosophical Series*).

To present the topic of this book, the key-position of physical science, as clearly as possible from the very beginning, the first chapter will attempt to show the important role which the development of physical science has played in the changing view man has taken of himself. Man's changed conception of himself has been greatly influenced by the whole of physical science and not merely by the biological theory of evolution. No matter how important this theory itself is for man's self-understanding, its influence has been as great as it is only because its tenets regarding man harmonized with man's new knowledge of himself acquired from other sources.

After indicating in the first two chapters the general framework in which we will consider the problem of evolution, Chapters Three to Seven will investigate the specific philosophical problems evoked by the theory of evolution in the narrow sense. The final chapters (Eight and Nine) will subsequently return to the more general problems.

CHAPTER ONE

THE CONTRIBUTION OF PHYSICAL SCIENCE TO THE CONTEMPORARY VIEW OF MAN

1. THE PARADOX OF PHYSICAL SCIENCE

A strange paradox confronts us when we ask what physical science has contributed to our view of man. Because this science is by its very nature dependent upon sense registrations, it has to remain on the "outside" of reality since only this side is accessible to the senses. Even if it wants to penetrate into what we call "the inside" of things, it is forced to turn this "inside" "outside," that is, open it up, as is done, for example, by the knife of the anatomist or by means of x-rays penetrating into a thing. In investigating material reality, however, this essential limitation of physical science is hardly felt as a restriction of our cognitive possibilities.

On the other hand, the situation is different when there is question of human reality. Even if a specialist in internal medicine turns us "inside out" by means of the most advanced scientific apparatus, we realize that all this barely touches the core of our person. Whatever he does to us, it always remains something peripheral insofar as the person is concerned. The core of the person can be contacted only by means of a human communication in which we "give" ourselves. In this contact sense experience still plays a role, for interhuman contact takes place in and through bodily behavior, speech and gestures. Nevertheless, the role played by man's sensitivity in this interpersonal contact is strikingly different from that in physical science.

We will not yet analyze this difference here, for such an analysis is not a simple matter. If we want to know exactly what physical science wants in its external registration of data, it is necessary to analyze the whole of physical science with respect to its experimental method and theoretical structure. And in a similar way, if we want to know what role is played by man's sensitivity in interpersonal contact, we have to consider extensively exactly what man's specifically human character is. Neither one nor the other analysis is very easy. For, strange as it may seem, there is no unanimity

15

about exactly what physical science is or what the specifically human character of man is. Provisionally, therefore, it appears safer to limit ourselves here to the primordial datum that we can learn about a person more effectively by having a conversation with him than by relying on the findings of an internal medical examination.

The same primordial datum lies also at the foundation of the distinction between the sciences of nature and *Geisteswissenschaften*. No matter how inadequate the term *Geisteswissenschaft* may be, the object of such a science is always man as embodied spirit. Hence the distinction between the two groups seems to be clear, in the sense that the *Geisteswissenschaften* always study the specifically human element and the sciences of nature do not study this element. One could expect, therefore, that the sciences of nature, the physical sciences, precisely because they remain "on the outside," can make hardly any essential contribution to man's self-knowledge and self-understanding.

However, this expectation is not confirmed by the actual course of history, in which physical science appears to have played a very important role with respect to man's self-knowledge. To understand that role correctly, attention must be paid not only to what physical science says about man insofar as he is its object but also to what it teaches us about man as a subject, i.e., as pursuing physical science. It is true, of course, that a consideration of man as pursuing physical science does not itself belong to physical science. Nevertheless, it is undeniable that what such a consideration reveals would never have been discovered without physical science.

On the other hand, the solution of this paradox—that physical science teaches us essential things about man despite the fact that it remains "peripheral"—cannot correctly be sought solely in what it tells us about man as a subject, as pursuing physical science. For even what it teaches us about man as an object reveals itself to be of essential importance. The most eloquent illustration of this point is the theory of evolution, which teaches that man has originated from living nature and that the latter itself has evolved from non-living reality. If the theory is true, it means that the study of nature is not as peripheral to man as was assumed in former times when man, to the extent that he is spiritual, was placed outside and in opposition to material reality.

Even if the theory of evolution is true, however, it does not mean that physical science gains much in importance through this modified view about man. For, even though material reality, as the source from which man has come, would have to be much more mysterious than it appears to be at first, it could very well be that this mysterious aspect of nature would be precisely something that physical science cannot study, since it is of necessity bounded by the "outside" of things. Here lies the probable reason why, for example, Teilhard de Chardin speaks about the need for a "hyper-physics" to make us sensitive to the mysterious "inside" or "within" of the thing of nature, their preconsciousness.[1] But, even if he is right, it still remains true that whatever this "hyperphysics" will reveal would not have come to light without ordinary physical science.

2. PHYSICAL SCIENCE CONCERNING MAN AS A SUBJECT

Here we will consider what physical science has taught us about man as its subject. In this consideration it will become evident also how closely that teaching is connected with its teaching about man as an object in the theory of evolution. The most important point that physical science has taught us about man as a subject undoubtedly is that it has confronted man, for the first time in history, with a progressive form of scientific knowledge. Let us develop this point here.

For the Greeks as well as for medieval man, science had a more or or less static character. They were aware of the limited character of human knowlege and, at the same time, conscious of the peculiar dialectics implied in this awareness of that limitation. For, by the very fact that they realized the limited character of human knowledge, they possessed a perspective pointing to unlimited knowledge and, therefore, to some extent transcended this limitation. However, they thought that the limits of what actually could be known, and therefore also of their perspective, were for once and for all immutably fixed by man's essence.

All this did not exclude a certain consciousness of history. Aristotle, for example, knew the history of philosophy and of science as they had developed before his time. However, he regarded that development as progress toward a certain ceiling which, because of man's limitations, could not be transcended. And if medieval men had con-

---

[1]Teilhard de Chardin, *The Phenomenon of Man*, New York, 1961, p. 30 (Torchbook ed.).

fidence in their synthesis of faith and science, this confidence was not based on being blissfully unaware of its relativity. However, they considered this relativity in reference to God's knowledge, which gave an almost concrete content to the old Greek philosophers' perspective upon infinity. They did not regard their knowledge as relative in reference to man's future knowledge.

This static view of science also explains why Aristotle could occupy such a prominent place in medieval philosophy and science. In a sense he had already reached the ceiling of what, humanly speaking, could be known. Medieval man's first and foremost aim was not so much to go beyond what Aristotle knew as to make a synthesis of his knowledge with God's revelation. The latter was likewise conceived in a static fashion. The same static view explains why medieval man had such a high regard for logic: he viewed it as the scientific tool *par excellence* because its function was to arrange in orderly fashion the science which was already given in principle.

Although logical coherence and arrangement also play an obviously important role in physical science, the center of gravity in the evolution of science has shifted to the discovery of new data. The dynamic character of physical science is intimately connected with its experimental character. For, as far as an experimental science is concerned, there is no field of experience that is given definitively, but this field is constantly expanded through experiments. For this reason questions are, in a sense, more important than answers in physical science. An answer, then, is only a genuine answer if it evokes new questions that can lead to new experiences. These new experiences do not necessarily concern data of reality that have been there always and were, so to speak, merely waiting to be discovered by man. On the contrary, the new experiences of an experimental science are concerned with a reality that is only called to realization in the experiment. Only through man's action, that is, his active interference with nature, nature realizes its potentialities; and only in and through this realization does nature make itself known to man.

In other words, the experimental science of nature does not primarily aim at increasing its knowledge of the given constellation of natural processes and forces; but it tends first and foremost toward penetrating into possibilities of nature, of which the existing constellations are relatively accidental realizations. For this reason the "artificial" experimental situations called forth by physical science are just as important for learning what nature is as those that are naturally present.

It stands to reason that the unique importance proper to the experimental character of physical science could not have been discovered at once when this science entered its period of bloom in the seventeenth century. It is always so in human history: only when things have assumed a clear-cut form and shape, is man able to see the importance of the first steps. For seventeenth century man the pursuit of physical science still remained primarily a cognitive activity. Hence it is not surprising that, confronted with the rise of physical science, the philosophical discussion of the seventeenth century centered at first on the question whether priority should be assigned to the senses or to the intellect. In this discussion empiricism appealed to the essentially empirical character of physical science, while rationalism sought support in the fact that mechanics, the best developed part of physical science, relied intensively on the use of mathematics. Both rationalism and empiricism, therefore, could adduce strong arguments in favor of their claims. An adequate evaluation of the knowledge given to man in physical science would have to take both aspects into account.

Immanuel Kant managed to overcome the opposition between rationalism and empiricism and assign to both their place in reference to the knowledge man acquires in physical science; but in the process he sacrificed its realistic character. For the dispute between empiricism and rationalism was permeated from the very start with another problem, viz., the question whether scientific knowledge makes us know reality as it is in itself. Kant opted for the subjective standpoint. All scientific knowledge, he said, is acquired by means of cognitive forms that are inherent to both sense knowledge and intellectual knowledge.

Later we will have the opportunity to revert to this idea of Kant, which made a powerful impression on philosophy. For the present we merely want to note that Kant's view, regardless of its truth value in other respects, certainly failed to do justice to physical science because he viewed this science solely as a cognitive activity. The experimental character of physical science, which demands so much attention for the operative aspect of the way in which knowledge is acquired, escaped Kant completely, for the simple reason that until the nineteenth century this aspect seemed to be of hardly any scientific importance.

Only in the course of the nineteenth century did it become evident that the experiment occupies a unique and irreplaceable position in physical science. Until then it had seemed to be not much more than a means to accelerate the process of induction. The varied observations on which induction has to be based in order to lead to the correct generalizations were often difficult to make. The experiment offered a quicker and easier but not essentially different approach. However, as experimental physical science developed, it became evident that the experiment gave access to and created realms of reality which would otherwise remain entirely beyond the reach of man's knowledge and which, nonetheless, were essential for a good understanding of realms that were "visible." For the acquisition and testing of knowledge, the hand that manipulates reality manifested itself just as important as the intellect and the senses.

In this way man's knowing was liberated from its isolation. To pursue physical science is a matter of the whole man, for his cognitive grasp of reality appears to depend upon his ability to interfere effectively in nature. The opposite also is true. The fact that, before the rise of physical science, the possibility to interfere in nature had only little scope was not caused by a fundamental powerlessness of man's hand with respect to nature, no matter how evident that powerlessness seemed to be. The true cause must be seen in the fact that the hand was regarded merely as the organ of simple experiential knowledge and not of scientific knowledge.

The remarkable point about this development of physical science into experimental science is that it restored, though on an incomparably higher level, the original unity of thinking and doing which is so characteristic of prescientific thinking and doing. And, even more remarkable, this higher level would never have been reached if the Greeks had not possessed the genius to see that they had to break the original unity of thinking and doing in order to pursue the ideal of pure and disinterested knowledge. If Euclid had not taken geometry out of its framework of the practical pursuit of measuring land and devoted himself to geometry for its own sake, mathematics would never have been able to make the decisive contributions to physical science and technology that it has made, continues to make, and will have to make in the future on an even grander scale. And if philosophy had not given man an awareness of his unique position in nature, physical science would never have been born.

The first break through the closed order, encompassing both man and cosmos, had to be a "spiritual" breakthrough in the form of pure and disinterested science. For a long time it seemed that this was the only possible breakthrough. Granted that man could place himself spiritually at a distance from the reality of nature, corporally he faced a nature that was overpowering and in which the limits of human activity seemed to have been laid down in principle as actual and concrete limits. Precisely this point, however, manifested itself as not true after the rise of physical science. This assertion may seem to be rather bold. Is it not true that man's activity still remains entirely dependent upon the limits imposed by nature? Have these limits been really enlarged so much?

There are two points to be kept in mind here. First of all, it is true that all human activity is really limited by the possibilities given in nature. Man cannot do more than utilize those possibilities, and it is beyond him to change nature. In this sense there are fundamental limits. However, and this is the second point, in all probability these fundamental limits do not have the character of being actual and concrete limits. As contemporary physical science teaches us, the transmutation of elementary particles makes it possible to make any kind of reality from any kind of reality; moreover, the equivalence of mass and energy offers the necessary energy in material reality to bring about such transformations. The perspectives opened by physical science as an experimental science are hardly limited perspectives. It opens up a second breakthrough, in which the original unity of man as embodied spirit is restored, for in this breakthrough man's bodily powerlessness with respect to his relationship to nature is also eliminated.

It is not our intention to speculate here about the possibilities opened by this perspective. A speculative reply to this question would be rather fruitless, anyhow, for these possibilities cannot be thought out but have to reveal themselves in practice. Here too the fundamentally experimental character of physical science makes itself felt. It exercises influence upon man not only with respect to his future, insofar as this future is directly marked with the seal of science and technology, but also with respect to the whole of human existence. Let us develop this point more in detail.

What the experimental character of physical science brings to light is not merely a specific feature of this science alone but something that is characteristic of human existence as such. It applies not only to the future but also to the past, not only to what will appear to be scientifically and technically possible but also to what will be possible for human life in general. Here also lies the explanation for the strange fact that, no matter how right the Greeks were in entering the road of pure and disinterested science, the inner consequences of their step remained hidden to them. Against their intentions, this road led to modern physical science with its eminently practical orientation. In other words, the pursuit of science itself was a new experience in which hitherto unforeseen possibilities disclosed themselves, in particular, the possibility that on a scientific level pure science and technique could go together.

This new experience itself had repercussions on the original self-experience with which man had plunged into the unknown adventure of science. Differently expressed, the second breakthrough has consequences for the first. This point deserves to be considered more in detail here.

The self-experience acquired in the pursuit of physical science makes man regard himself differently from the way he could formerly view himself. This difference is not merely a matter of aspects that concern man as the subject pursuing physical science precisely insofar as he is a subject pursuing physical science, but refers to general aspects. True, these aspects revealed themselves first in the pursuit of physical science, but they were later recognized as typical of human existence as such. The progressive character of human knowledge disclosed itself first in physical science, but since then man has become convinced that progressiveness is valid for the whole of human existence. It could hardly have been different. For the self-experience man has acquired in the development of physical science essentially touches his relationship with nature, and a modification of his view of nature automatically has consequences for man's view of himself.

If nature is not a formation that is given for once and for all but something to be transformed and realized, then man is the being whose task it is to bring the hidden possibilities of nature to realization. Nature is not merely something that is given and as such presents man's cognitive power with a task, but it is also in its totality a task for man's power of action which is unbreakably united with his power of cognition. Hence, like science, culture is not a matter that concerns almost solely man's spirit and with respect to which the body and its techniques would merely have the subservient function of making the earthly life of the human spirit possible. Culture is the all-encompassing activity of man as spirit-in-matter, as embodied spirit, in which the spirit brings about its self-realization in and through matter by bringing the hidden possibilities of matter to realization.

As a consequence of this new way of looking at man, contemporary philosophy, in spite of its diverse trends, shows great unanimity in its rejection of a dualistic conception of man, such as even a man like Descartes continued to defend. This unanimity is not the result of independent philosophical discussions but a consequence of philosophical reflection upon a new self-experience of man. This fact gives hope for the future. If it is possible for man to discover more about himself in his growing self-experience than was originally given to him, then this possibility can have consequences also for the future of philosophy. For, then, philosophical disagreement would not have to be based upon accepting the permanent impossibility of understanding man himself thoroughly or at least of putting his self-experience in words. It could very well be that provisionally man does not yet have enough self-experience, simply because he is not yet the man he should be.

Man's insufficient openness to the question of being (*Sein*) as a human question would perhaps also have to be attributed to his initial inability to question be-ings (*Seiende*) in the correct way. As the history of philosophy shows, man quickly realized the importance of the all-encompassing question of being. Perhaps, however, he was not able to ask that question with sufficient purity because the question cannot be isolated but has to be put in connection with man's concrete questions regarding the various be-ings. And with respect to these concrete questions, he was at first barely able to raise any of them. He still had to learn the correct way of questioning.

3. Physical Science Concerning Man as Object

All this shows to what extent the things which physical science has taught about man as a subject prepared the way for what this science in its theory of evolution teaches us about man as an object. This theory regards man as the result of a natural process of development. Biologists are generally in agreement with respect to the matter, even though the "how" of evolution and especially the last phase, the "leap" from animal to man, remains a great mystery. In its own way, then, the theory of evolution complements what we already knew about man as the subject of physical science, viz., that he is not a static being but a self-unfolding, self-realizing being. Although it may be true that the course of evolution before the appearance of man differed from that after his appearance, there remains a common element. Man's self-realization and self-development in history somehow is connected with a preceding development in the "history" of nature, which made the appearance of man possible.

There are here, of course, all kinds of difficult problems, such as whether it is correct to speak of "history" with respect to a prehuman development. Likewise, how would one have to conceive an unfolding and development of infrahuman reality into a human reality? These questions will occupy our attention later. At present we merely want to record that the connection between the natural evolution into man and human history as development are given within the sphere of physical science itself.

True, what physical science teaches us about man as its subject is not itself an object considered by physical science. What we have said about it in the preceding pages constitutes a philosophical reflection *upon* physical science rather than a scientific consideration made by this science. All this, however, does not take away from the fact that what has been disclosed in this way would never have come to light without physical science. In other words, speaking about the evolution of natural reality and speaking about the evolution of human reality is not speaking about two entirely different and unconnected spheres. Physical science binds these spheres together. It occupies a key-position.

For a correct appreciation of this key-position it is necessary first to examine the importance of physical science for philosophy or, expressed in more general terms, the relationship between science and philosophy.

CHAPTER TWO

PHYSICAL SCIENCE AND PHILOSOPHY

1. THE LABORIOUS PREHISTORY OF PHYSICAL SCIENCE

As we have seen in the preceding chapter, man's first break through the bounds encompassing both nature and man was philosophical. By asking the philosophical question about himself, man placed himself at a distance from nature, he became conscious of the fact that he was not merely a part of nature. Without this philosophical question no *science* of nature could have arisen out of the primitive knowledge of nature and techniques that man possessed of old. Philosophy, especially Greek philosophy, created the intellectual climate in which physical science could be born. Such a science could arise only where man possessed a certain vision of nature and its mode of knowability. It may surprise us at first that, after the creation of the necessary climate, a very long period—about two thousand years—was needed before physical science did arise; but on closer inspection this astonishment disappears.

The reason is as follows. Physical science is an inductive-deductive science. The combination of inductive and deductive characteristics contains a peculiar paradox, which disappears as soon as the science is able to function but which leads to almost invincible difficulties in trying to get it started. These difficulties lie in the fact that the necessary theoretical principles of the deductions have to be discovered by way of empirical inductions, regardless of whether the latter are experimental or not. But precisely in order to make the appropriate inductions it is necessary to have theoretical principles. One who does not want to drown in a limitless ocean of data must know beforehand what is relevant when he begins to observe or experiment. This necessity does not cause too much trouble when a science already exists, for in that case enough principles are known to distinguish the relevant from the irrelevant with respect to a problem. At the inception of a new science, however, this mutual implication creates the greatest difficulties.[1]

---

[1]For a detailed study of this problem cf. van Melsen, *Science and Technology,* Pittsburgh, 1961, Chapters I-VI.

Here lies the reason why the most important achievements of the Greeks were accomplished in those realms in which the distinction between the relevant and the irrelevant did not offer too much difficulty. Such was the case in the formal sciences, such as logic (Aristotle) and mathematics (Euclid), and in the branches of physical science in which the mathematically relevant element disclosed itself readily, such as astronomy (Ptolemy) or the theory of equilibrium (Archimedes). Thus it is not surprising that the growth of physical science in the seventeenth century resulted from the idea of applying the theoretical mechanical insights acquired in astronomy to the terrestrial motions of fall and throw.

It is also in the light of the inductive-deductive character of physical science that one should look at the controversy between rationalism and empiricism which arose when physical science began to develop. The rationalists were keenly aware of the necessity of giving priority to theory, *in casu* mathematical theory (Descartes), while the empiricists were just as keenly aware of the necessity of assigning priority to sense experience (Bacon). On first sight, these two priorities seem to exclude each other on more than superficial grounds. If the exclusion had been merely superficial, physical science would have appeared much sooner in the history of human culture. Nonetheless, the exclusion was merely an apparent one, as is evidenced by the fact that, from the seventeenth century on, physical science developed very rapidly. Accordingly, the reason why physical science was so slow in getting started must not be sought in the Greek attitude of mind, but in the paradoxical character of physical science as an inductive-deductive discipline.

Although the Greeks had the correct scientific attitude, the late development of physical science led to a mistake in the Greek and medieval general theory of science. More specifically, their theory of science failed to make room for the progressive character of science because they were acquainted only with sciences whose principles could be readily abstracted from experience and were, therefore, regarded as established for once and for all.

2. Two Types of Principles of Physical Science

In a study devoted to the relationship between philosophy and physical science it is necessary to examine the concept "principle of science" somewhat more profoundly, for the expression is rather ambiguous. Considering contemporary physical science, one may say that it is based on the principle of the conservation of energy. At the same time, however, one can also say that, being an experimental science, it is based on the principle that the ultimate criterion lies in the experimental data. In both cases the term "principle" is used, but its meaning is not all the same. In the case of the conservation principle there is question of a principle that has been inductively established and is used in all kinds of theoretical deductions but that, nonetheless, remains fundamentally subject to experimental critique. In other words, it remains possible that in the future physical science will reject or modify the principle. As a matter of fact, this principle has been repeatedly modified in the past. No matter how fundamental it may be, it belongs to the content of physical science and as such is directly subject to the judgment and critique of physical science.

The second above-mentioned principle is entirely different. It does not belong to the content of physical science but may be called one of its constituent principles. It characterizes physical science as an experimental science. Or to express it differently, the principle does not express anything about what physical science discovers in material reality, but makes a statement regarding the method man must follow in his study of material phenomena. It expresses a general aspect of man's way of knowing.

Just as there are many principles of physical science that belong to the content of this science, so also are there many that are constituent principles with respect to the method of this science. The latter do not merely refer to aspects of man's knowledge that are relevant to physical science, but may also say something about the general character of nature, the object of physical science. Let us add an example of the last-named type.

Physical science starts from the principle that the phenomena it studies can be repeated or at least can be analyzed in repeatable aspects. Without this presupposition induction and experimentation would be meaningless. The method of physical science, therefore, contains a certain view of nature; and this view precedes everything that physical science subsequently establishes as the concrete scientific content of the material phenomena. Because this view is embodied in its method, physical science does not explicitly develop this view. It implicitly retains this view of man and of nature as something constituent of its method, as something that makes physical science be what it is.

This implicit view is ultimately due to the philosophical efforts of the old Greeks to arrive at a clear understanding of the relationship between man and nature. The insight into this relationship preceded, therefore, the actual successful pursuit of physical science. On the other hand, from what we have said in the preceding chapter it is evident how important the rise of physical science in the seventeenth century has been for a more profound understanding of this relationship. We are touching here a crucial point in the relationship between philosophy and physical science, which several reasons compel us to examine more in detail. Only a carefully differentiated consideration can help us find clarity in this matter. To begin with, we will have to consider the extreme views regarding the relationship between physical science and philosophy.

3. DIFFERENT VIEWS REGARDING THE RELATIONSHIP BETWEEN PHYSICAL SCIENCE AND PHILOSOPHY

The first of the two extreme views regarding the relationship between philosophy and physical science considers them as two entirely different disciplines, two fundamentally distinct ways of approaching reality, which have nothing in common and therefore are hardly able to help each other. The second view holds that philosophy is wholly dependent upon the condition of physical science. Insofar as it admits that there is a philosophical approach to problems, it stresses that this approach is totally dependent upon physical science for its necessary data. Solid arguments can be adduced for both these views.

Strong arguments in favor of the first view have already been given at the beginning of this chapter. The philosophical principles that are constitutive of physical science and embodied in its method can hardly be contradicted by physical science itself because, as physical science, it is based upon these principles. No matter what unexpected discoveries physical science may make, they will always remain within the limits of the philosophical vision that lies at the foundation of the method proper to physical science. This vision is based upon a primary experience of nature and of man and cannot be transcended by any subsequent developments of physical science. The importance and the unique character of this primary and original vision are best illustrated by an example, which at the same time will give us an opportunity to show how much empirical data needs a theoretical context to be fruitful.

Until the modern era man was convinced that water, if heated, changed into air. This conviction was based upon serious empirical grounds, for one can observe that steam disappears in the air. Artlessly formulated, the empirical judgment, "Water if heated changes into air," is beyond reproach. The fact that, in the new era, objections were made against this judgment finds its explanation in the theoretical interpretation of the judgment rather than its simple expression of an observation. For in Greek and medieval science this interpretation was made within the framework of the theory of four elements. The element water became the element air. But this interpretation appeared sterile. To become fruitful, a new theoretical interpretation was needed, which rejected the theory of four elements and substituted another theory. The new theory did not regard water and air as elements but as composite substances having, moreover, compositions of a different type. In this new interpretation the judgment expressing the phenomenon in question became: "Water if heated becomes water vapor," which is a component part of the mixture "air." In the light of the currently accepted physical principles, this new formula is still valid and the old interpretation seems definitively faulty.

These few remarks, however, do not tell the whole story of the two judgments in question. A closer analysis shows that, in spite of the explicit difference in the scientific interpretation of the empirical datum, there is an implicit element that remains unchanged in the two judgments. Both judgments are general, for they express something about water as such. They state that water always reacts in the same way when it is heated. In other words, both assume that material reality has a repeatable structure. This structure, as we have seen, is connected with a view of nature that lies at the foundation of the scientific method as such. This view was not changed when physical science arrived at a new idea concerning evaporation. The reason for this is that the view in question is not explicitly formulated in the judgment made by physical science. It is likewise not methodically investigated in the pursuit of this science.

In physical science itself the view remains implicit. As soon as it is made explicit, we are no longer in physical science but in philosophy. Let us add at once that in the explicitation markedly different opinions manifest themselves. These range from an interpretation which regards the universality of the judgments in question as primarily a matter of language, to others which profess to see here a structure of reality. No matter what one thinks about these interpretations—we will discuss the multiplicity of philosophies later--, one thing seems certain, viz., that we are dealing here with a realm of problems that is more fundamental than those which are explicitly considered by physical science.

This realm seems to be an area for autonomous philosophical reflection, that is, for a kind of reflection that can, in principle, remain outside the development of physical science because the latter stays wholly within the framework of the primary and original data of experience embodied in its method. The autonomous character of philosophical problematics also explains why the old Greek philosophical discussions remain very pertinent in many respects, as well as the fact that, at least with respect to asking philosophical questions, there is something that may appropriately be referred to as "perennial philosophy."

There are, however, also strong arguments in favor of the thesis that the development of physical science exercises an influence upon the discussions of philosophy and, in particular, upon the view of the relationship between man and nature on which the method of physical science is based. For, as we have seen in Chapter One, the evolution of physical science into experimental science, together with the possibilities of interfering technically in the order of nature which revealed themselves in that evolution, has given man a new view of his relationship with nature. Man's spiritual mastery of nature in purely disinterested science revealed itself capable of becoming a spiritual-corporeal mastery through theoretical-practical science. Thus it is not surprising that the history of philosophy, despite the latter's autonomy, is strongly marked by the development of physical science.

As a matter of fact, the history of physical science and that of philosophy show much interaction. They reveal in particular that philosophy, when left to itself, is easily affected by sterility but flourishes when philosophical thought is confronted with other ways of thinking. Such confrontations occurred when philosophy encountered theology (the patristic period), Arabian learning and science (thirteenth century), nascent physical science as an autonomous discipline (seventeenth century), and the rise of the science of history (nineteenth century). It occurs in our time again, as philosophy faces the crisis situations existing in the sciences of nature and of man.

It seems as if the reply to philosophy's questioning, when left all by itself, loses its dynamic tension and degenerates into empty verbalism. Could the reason for this curious situation lie perhaps in this, that, like the answer of physical science, the philosophical answer is fruitful only when it gives rise to new questions—questions which cannot be answered independently of physical science and other empirical sciences or, more generally, independently of history? An affirmative reply does not necessarily go counter to the distinction between physical science and philosophy defended in the preceding pages, although it is true that it makes this distinction more or less relative. This relativity can be explained in several ways.

In a previously published book,[2] in which we devoted much space to the relationship between physical science and the philosophy of nature, this relativity was explained mainly as follows. In theory the problems of philosophy and those of physical science can be sharply distinguished, but in practice man cannot make this distinction with all possible sharpness. For this reason, the philosophical explicitation of primary and original experience will of necessity always be influenced by prescientific, primitive-scientific or antiquated scientific data. In other words, authentic primary experience will always be mixed with elements that do not belong to it, but the non-authentic character of these elements will come to light only through the development of physical science. In this indirect way, therefore, the evolution of physical science can contribute to the clarification and purification of philosophical problematics. In the following chapter we will meet with many examples illustrating this function of physical science.

On the other hand, it is also true that physical science is never pure. The physicist, chemist or biologist will always place his physical theories and data against a background of certain philosophical convictions. A classical example is provided by mechanism, which accompanied physical science from the seventeenth to the twentieth centuries. In the eyes of many, mechanism, which assumed that material reality is composed of immutable primeval elements and therefore regarded all changes as new arrangements of these elements, was an intrinsic part of physical science itself. As a matter of fact, however, it was a philosophical addition, which could be removed by a careful philosophical analysis. While that analysis cannot offer any aid in solving the proper problems of physical science itself, it can contribute to the purification of scientific thinking in general.

---

[2]*The Philosophy of Nature,* Pittsburgh, 4th impr., 1961, Chapters I and III.

4. The Philosophical Importance of the Evolution of Physical Science

The preceding considerations certainly do not indicate the only way in which physical science and philosophy can influence each other. The case of mechanism clearly shows this. The fact that mechanism has become discredited among scientists is not so much the result of critique exercised by philosophy from without as of the evolution of physical science itself. This evolution showed that mechanism was untenable because the absolute value of mechanical models, such as the wave model and the particle model, had to be rejected for purely scientific reasons.

The objection could be made that mechanism as a philosophical theory did not arise solely from a philosophical attempt to explain the changeable character of material reality, but was also concretely co-determined by all kinds of now antiquated scientific ideas. In other words, the contribution made by the development of physical science consisted in laying bare the antiquated character of those scientific ideas rather than in offering an original philosophical idea. The truth of this objection can perhaps be conceded. In any case, however, it shows that a centuries-old philosophical tradition could be unmasked only thanks to the evolution of physical science. True, even before the recent development of physical science, it may have been possible to show that scientific theories do not necessarily have to be interpreted in a mechanistic fashion. *De facto,* however the arguments lacked power of persuasion.

A question that inevitably arises here is whether any purely philosophical argument carries enough power of persuasion. Looking at the many differences of opinion in philosophy, one could say that this power appears to be lacking. The entire history of philosophy bears witness to this fact. The question touches a delicate point—delicate, especially because here there is also a strange paradox. To see this paradox, let us return to the above-mentioned example of the evaporation of water.

As we have seen, the statement, "Water when heated becomes water vapor," contains two judgments, one explicit and the other implicit. The explicit judgment is a judgment of physical science, which has replaced an antiquated explicit judgment of physical science stating that water becomes air. The implicit judgment, however, remained the same. This implicit philosophical judgment, moreover, referred not so much to water in particular as to things and events of nature in general. The paradox here is that the implicit philosophical judgment is much more solid than the explicit scientific judgment.

History itself clearly shows this. The former explicit scientific judgment has been replaced by another. Although the latter is now generally affirmed, we must remember that in principle there is always the possibility of a subsequent modification due to the progress of physical science. The implicit judgment, on the other hand, has not been changed by the development of physical science and will not be changed by any subsequent scientific progress. The reason is that the implicit judgment refers to an aspect of material reality which makes this reality accessible to the scientific method. We do not mean to say, of course, that the implicit judgment is absolutely inviolable, but only that it cannot be overthrown by the development of physical science, for it is concerned with a constituent principle of this science. As long as physical science proceeds inductively, it will have to remain faithful to this principle.

Accordingly, there can be no doubt that the implicit judgment, and the philosophical principle which it contains, are more certain than any judgment or principle whatsoever of physical science. Nevertheless, experience seems to show that scientific judgments and principles offer much more certainty than philosophical judgments. The explanation of this paradox is that the greater certainty belonging to the philosophical judgment refers only to the judgment insofar as it remains implicit. As soon as we attempt to formulate it explicitly, all kinds of philosophical divergencies make themselves felt. Man seems to be powerless here. Philosophical principles seem to possess an intuitive certainty as long as they are "lived," as they are here in the pursuit of physical science. But they lose this certainty as soon as man endeavors to explicitate them.

This strange phenomenon could be regarded as a plea for letting philosophy be—as its name says—a "desire for wisdom" and to concentrate all attention upon physical science, because it appears impossible to get anywhere with philosophy. However, first of all, it is not possible to give up philosophy; and secondly, even if it were possible, it would lead to unacceptable consequences.

That it is not possible to give up philosophy is proven by the history of positivism. Positivism tried to limit man's meaningful knowledge to positive science. To do so, it had to reflect explicitly upon the positive sciences and their constituent principles. This reflection automatically gave positivism a place in the history of philosophy as one of its innumerable phases. The only way to escape from this consequence would be to let the philosophical question dissolve itself into thin air in a spontaneous act of disappearance, for any explicit act would be philosophical. But such a spontaneous disappearance of the philosophical question would mean that man had given up being-man. For the philosophical question is nothing else but man's question about himself; it is precisely this question that makes him man. Also, this question is ultimately the question that animates physical science. Science also would disappear if man would no longer understand the question about himself.

However, even if the impossible were possible and physical science would continue to exist, man would become merely its unconscious executor because the question of meaning would have disappeared. He would be pursuing physical science without knowing what he is doing. Although man would be a new link in the process of the evolution due to technical possibilities of development disclosed by physical science, he himself, inwardly, would not be involved in the process. He would be at the mercy of technical possibilities without a will of his own, without being able or permitted to ask himself which of these possibilities should be realized and how they should be realized, on any other grounds than those of physical science and technology.

The preceding remarks about the physical sciences would apply also to the human sciences. They, too, could be pursued only in a scientific-technical way. However, an additional problem would arise here, for they are differently related to philosophy than is physical science, at least if we judge the matter on the basis of our present experience. In physical science there exists *de facto* unanimity about the method to be followed. Its method is constituted by implicit principles that are not discussed in physical science itself. These principles may cause difficulties and divergent opinions as soon as man tries to explicitate them philosophically, but all this does not prevent man from handling the method of physical science successfully. In the human sciences, on the other hand, such a *de facto* unanimity about the method to be followed does not exist. Phenomenologists, existentialists, positivists and marxists each have not only their own philosophical view about this method but often also pursue the human sciences in their own way. For this reason there exist in the human sciences schools of thoughts and trends whose differences arise from divergent philosophical views of man and man's cognitive possibilities.[3]

Something of this divergency begins to manifest itself even in biology, as is evidenced by the controversy between vitalism and mechanism. We will consider all this in detail, but merely wish to note here that the divergency manifesting itself in philosophy is not limited to philosophy but emerges also in the human sciences. In addition, it reveals itself in all kind of fundamental questions that are raised as soon as one considers the way in which the application of physical science and technology changes man's earthly existence. If we leave biology out of consideration for the present, it is only in physical science proper that the philosophical division does not make itself felt. This exceptional situation of physical science creates at least a special problem for philosophical reflection; but, even more important, it points to a certain key position of physical science in the sense that this science offers man a possible way of progressing to the solution of his difficulties.

Physical science is evidently a limited science, a science having only a restricted scope, and therefore unable to give a satisfactory answer to all our questions. As we have seen in the preceding chapter, however, despite its restricted character, its peculiar and unphilosophical way of approaching reality, physical science gives answers that indirectly contribute to the philosophical clarification of the philosophical question concerning man himself. Although physical science does not explicitly either ask or answer the philosophical question, nevertheless, its development appears to be, in an implicit way, a kind of explicitation of the original philosophical views embodied in it.

We readily grant that the formula used here to express this aspect of the relationship between science and philosophy is rather complex and difficult. Yet it covers the situation rather aptly. Physical science is directly interested only in its own problems, as these arise in the perspective of its methodical investigation of material reality. This method itself, however, is inspired by a certain view of nature and of man. And as the method of physical science discloses new realms of research, the value of this method becomes increasingly more evident and may reveal consequences that at first could not have been foreseen.

---

[3] Cf. Chapter VIII.

The most eloquent example of such consequences is the experimental and technical possibilities which today appear in the perspective of physical science and which present us with such an entirely different picture of the relationship between man and nature. In a certain sense it is true, of course, that one and the same fundamental methodic attitude has led from simple experimenting to modern nuclear research. All principles of this method have remained the same. Nevertheless, with respect to the philosophical view of the relationship between man and nature, it makes a difference whether man is helpless in relation to the constellations of forces occurring in nature because his bodily powers are weak or is able to modify any natural constellation by his purposive interference. Physical science remains faithful to its original principles because it remains faithful to its method; but the new possibilities disclosed by the method, nevertheless, constitute an imposing explicitation of the implicit content of this method.

However, this explicitation remains "implicit" because man does not actively appropriate the new view of the relationship between nature and man, resulting from the evolution of physical science, until he philosophically reflects upon this science. The explicit philosophical explicitation is, of course, exposed to the same dangers that always threaten philosophy, such as absolutizing a particular situation existing in physical science and making it an irrevocable norm. The "implicit" explicitation, likewise, does not lead to unanimity; but it does offer an unexpected yet welcome perspective, viz., that, for the solution of its problems, philosophy need not rely solely upon its own forces but can be effectively aided by the "lived experience" of physical science. Of essential importance in this matter is also the conviction of physical science that it has hardly begun its work. This conviction expresses itself especially in connection with the state of the question that is to occupy us more particularly in this book—the theory of evolution.

Even today, a century after Darwin's publication of *The Origin of Species,* evolution is more a question than an answer. The main difference between Darwin's time and ours is not so much that we know much more about evolution now as that evolution is now generally accepted. Besides, there is a strange kind of contrast between the biologist's faith in evolution and his inability to explain evolution. This inability does not arise only from the historical character of the theory of evolution, although this character causes its own type of difficulties. (A much more important reason for his inability to explain the theory of evolution is that it is the counterpart of another inability of the biologist, viz., in explaining the phenomena of life and living structures physically and chemically.) Although progress has been made in this matter, this progress is more impressive as a promise of things to come than as actual achievement.

Even this inability, however, may be regarded as hopeful for philosophy. Perhaps the human adventure has merely started, not only with respect to the scales of time which the theory of evolution uses to measure the past, but also with respect to the future when calculated with an appropriate scale of time. We mean a scale which suggests itself when we try to see the little knowledge we now have in contrast with the multitude of questions that can be raised by man, in physical science as well as in other realms. Viewed in this perspective, the lack of unanimity in philosophy suddenly appears in a different light. If we pay attention to the multiplicity and especially the depth of questions asked in philosophy, we are no longer surprised that the answers still lack unanimity. The ability to ask these questions now appears more important than the lack of unanimity. The latter may even be regarded as a fortunate sign that man wants to keep many roads open, that he wants to try in many different ways to advance.

One of these ways is the way of physical science, for, in spite of its one-sidedness and abstractness, it teaches us much about man and his world. Its contribution consists not only in its direct discoveries concerning man and his world but also, and even especially, in the subject matter which its development offers for philosophical reflection. (In this way it provides indirect replies to many philosophical problems. In the first chapter we considered especially what physical science teaches us about man as the subject of science. In the following chapters the main emphasis will fall upon what physical science tells us about man as an object of this science, that is, about man as a being of nature, a being that has originated from nature by a process of evolution.) Here also it will become evident that the development of physical science has made important contributions to the clarification of typically philosophical problems. These questions, moreover, are not only directly concerned with man but also with all realms of being, with living non-human reality as well as with non-living reality. And through these realms of being, these questions also let the question of being itself appear in a new way.

CHAPTER THREE

THE CONCEPT OF MATTER

1. Introduction

If there is any concept which one could expect to be directly discussed by physical science, the concept of matter would undoubtedly be named. Surely, one would argue, among all the sciences, physics and chemistry are those which occupy themselves most intensively with the study of material reality and therefore are likely to devote much attention to the concept of matter. In a similar way, biology would have to be regarded as the science that can most appropriately enlighten us about the concept of life.

These expectations, however, are not fulfilled. In physics and chemistry the concept of matter enters, at most, as a marginal concept. Biology, it is true, speaks much more about the concept of life than physics and chemistry discuss that of matter. The reason probably is that the biologist feels compelled to circumscribe the object of his interest in relation to other physical sciences, while the physicist and chemist do not feel this need. Wherever there are material phenomena, whether in the realm of the living or that of the non-living, the physicist and the chemist encounter their object; hence they do not feel the necessity of making distinctions as strongly as the biologist does.[1]

Generally speaking, however, the biologist will limit himself to the enumeration of certain characteristics proper to life. The philosopher, at any rate, who wants to find out exactly what life is and consults biological treatises, is usually disappointed. He finds that those treatises remain much too concerned with marginal points. He is even more disappointed if he addresses himself to the physicist or the chemist to see what they mean by matter, for he does not even receive any direct reply to his question. The measure of his disappointment depends, of course, also on his philosophical orientation and especially on his ideas concerning the relationship between philosophy and physical science.

---

[1] "It has been said that if you scratch a biologist you find a philosopher under the skin." W. H. Thorpe, *Biology and the Nature of Man,* Oxford, 1962, p. IX.

It may even happen that he is not disappointed at all because he is firmly convinced that the question of what matter is, is not at all a question to be answered by physical science but a philosophical question. In that case, the inability of physical science to reply to his question simply serves to confirm him in his philosophical conviction. Another reason why he may not feel disappointed by physical science may be, not because he expects the answer to be given by a more or less autonomous philosophy, but because he suspects that, as a science in development, physical science has not yet reached the stage in which it can supply the answer. In other words, he regards the question of what matter is as a question belonging to physical science, although not yet answerable by it.

From our remarks in the preceding chapter concerning the relationship between philosophy and physical science, it should be evident that we regard both of these positions as too one-sided. (The question of what matter is, is, we believe, a philosophical question; but on the other hand, the answer to this question cannot be given independently of physical science and its development.) For, the reply to that question lies contained in the methodic attitude of questioning proper to physical science. The most profound intentions of this attitude, however, reveal themselves fully only in the development of physical science. For this reason any philosophical answer retains a provisional character, at least to the extent that the road to further developments must be kept open.

In the philosophy of the past this aspect of openness was less emphasized than it is now, although man was aware of the relative character of his philosophical answers. The reason for this lesser emphasis lies in the fact that, at the time, physical science had not yet sufficiently revealed its character as an evolving science. Kant, whose philosophy is so strongly marked by reflection upon the new physical science, does not show any trace of being aware of its evolving character, a fact that undoubtedly is connected with his failure to recognize the experimental character of physical science.

It is interesting in this context to see what Hegel says about the matter. Hegel acknowledges that physical science has a preparatory task with respect to philosophy. "Philosophy," he says, "must not only be in harmony with the experience of nature, but the origin and development of the philosophical science has physics as a presupposition and condition. However, the process of origin and the preparatory stages of a science should not be confused with that science itself. In the science itself they can no longer appear as foundations; for here that foundation should rather be the necessity of the concept itself."[2]

This passage could obviously be written only by someone who was convinced that physical science as empirical science was in a way complete, for only then would it be able to fulfill the preparatory function ascribed to it by Hegel. Since it is an experimental science that constantly expands and develops its field of experience, physical science will never be able to perform the preparatory task Hegel attributed to it at least not in the way in which he conceived it; because then openness to the future would characterize not only physical science but also philosophy. Hegel, we may add, was not alone in his misconception of what physical science is, for the view held by him was typical of his time.[3]

If no definitive answer can be given to the question of what matter is, this admission does not mean that no answer whatsoever can be given. As a matter of fact, many beginnings of an answer were given even in ancient Greek philosophy. In the following pages we will collect them, see how they were embodied in the methodic attitude of research proper to physical science, and then investigate what consequences the development of physical science has had for the reply to the question of what matter is. A particularly interesting aspect of this inquiry will show how much richer is the implicit view that physical science has of matter than are the explicitly formulated views of the philosophers and scientists of the new era.

The survey that follows here serves not only to confirm what we have said regarding the relationship between physical science and philosophy, but also shows to what extent man's developing thought about matter has prepared for the theory of evolution.

2. GREEK AND MEDIEVAL THOUGHT ABOUT MATTER

On many problems, a study concerning Greek and medieval thought must always take into consideration that the separation between

---

[2]*Enzyklopädie der philosophischen Wissenschaften,* par. 246: "Nicht nur muss die Philosophie mit der Naturerfahrung übereinstimmend sein, sondern die Entstehung und Bildung der philosophischen Wissenschaft hat die empirische Physik zur Voraussetzung und Bedingung. Ein anderes aber ist der Gang des Entstehens und die Vorarbeiten einer Wissenschaft, ein anderes die Wissenschaft selbst; in dieser können jene nicht mehr als Grundlage erscheinen, welche hier vielmehr die Notwendigkeit des Begriffs sein soll."

[3]It continued to exist for a long time after Hegel. As Max Planck relates, his teachers expressed the idea that physical science was largely complete. Cf. Planck, *Wege zur physikalischen Erkenntnis,* Leipzig, 2nd ed., 1934, p. 128.

philosophy and physical science had not yet taken place. Here and there one can discover a beginning of such a separation, but it does not go beyond a first hesitant step. In a certain sense, the absence of that separation makes it easier to study Greek and medieval thought. But this simplification does not mean that there were no divergencies of views. Without them, Greek and medieval thought would never have possessed the great value that they had for later times, for divergencies force men to reflect and express in their own way an openness of mind which is the indispensable basis of progress.

It is not surprising, therefore, that there were divergencies in Greek thought about matter. Particularly striking is the fact that the term "matter" had a twofold meaning and referred either to concretely existing reality as such or to a certain aspect of it.

According to Aristotle, who developed especially the second sense of the term "matter," matter does not exist by itself but is only a capacity to receive a form. Concrete things are composed of matter and form. The statement, therefore, that something is a *material* being merely expresses that it is a non-simple being, but says nothing about the place such a being occupies in the scale of inorganic, organic and human realities. The kind of a being something is does not depend upon matter but on the form. The fact that matter is that which has received form accounts for the changeable character of the beings "composed" of matter and form.

Let us add that for Aristotle matter and form are analogous concepts. Sometimes matter itself already includes some determinations, at other times not (so-called "prime matter"). All meanings of matter, however, have in common the capacity to be further determined. Hence, the concept of matter is always something relative and always refers to the corresponding form. As prime matter, matter refers to form in the sense of the substantial form determining the essence. As matter in the sense of clay, marble and similar materials, it refers to form as an external shape.

A different concept of matter is found in Democritus. For him, matter is the concrete being itself, viz., the atoms. He opposes matter as the full to the void, that is, the empty space in which the atoms can move. This power to move is the ground of the only change that the atoms can undergo. In themselves, they are wholly immutable and consequently also eternal. The only further determinations of which they are capable—to express the point in terms of the Aristotelian matter-form schema—are configurations, mutual arrangements

of position; but these remain extrinsic to the material beings themselves. These beings are intrinsically untouched by these configurations, they remain exactly what they are.

We must add that the power to move is a "native" property
of the atoms, it is an active power and the basis of all changes in the
material world. We can see here the first beginning of an idea that
would subsequently become very important in the development of
physical science. (The latter also starts with the idea that matter has
an inner activity of its own and thus assumes a position that is more
or less contrary to Aristotelian thought.)

While for Aristotle the concept of matter was purely relative, Plato
(especially in *Timaeus*) and the Platonic tradition ascribe to matter
a kind of autonomous existence, at least in the sense that matter
appears as the negative, as that which resists the idea.[4] This meaning received special emphasis in the Christian tradition, not only in
the time that this tradition was given a largely Platonic orientation
by Augustine, but also in the later Middle Ages which, philosophically speaking, were more Aristotelian. In the Christian tradition
matter was opposed to spirit as the lower to the higher. The idea
that matter also is created by God caused little change in this general
sphere of thinking about matter.

Even for Thomas Aquinas, matter was the non-intelligible and
somehow acting contrary to form. He says, for example, that the
occurrence of misformed beings in nature must be attributed to the
causal influence of matter.[5] It seems as if, for Thomas Aquinas, in
spite of himself, matter has a kind of independent existence. We do
not mean in the same way as for Democritus. For, in Thomas, matter
always refers to form, it always remains an aspect of the concretely
existing material being; it makes this being changeable and individual-
izes it, since the same specific form can be realized more than once,
or rather can be materialized repeatedly. Because of the matter-form
composition, there can be a plurality of individuals of the same
species. Yet it seems that the form's need to become materialized is
regarded as the cause of the form's realization meeting sometimes
with partial failure.[6]

---

[4]Cf. M. Van Straaten, "Het hylemorphisme in de antieke wijsbegeerte,"
Studia catholica, 1952, pp. 237-255.

[5]"Et propter hoc vidimus quod ea quae reducuntur in materiam sicut in
primam causam, sunt praeter intentionem agentis, sicut monstra et alia pec-
cata naturae." *Contra Gentiles,* bk. II, ch. 40.

[6]Concerning this question see H. Dolch, *Kausalität im Verständnis des Theologen und der Begründer neuzeitlicher Physik,* Freiburg i.Br., 1954, pp. 77-92.

There is another point that deserves our attention here. As we have noted above, for Democritus matter has an active power, but not for Aristotle and Thomas Aquinas, at least if we abstract from the resistance matter offers to form, which is a Platonic rather than an Aristotelian element. However, no matter how much truth there is in the opposition between Democritus' concept of matter and that of Aristotle—to limit ourselves to these two—it does not follow that according to the Aristotelian view inorganic *reality* must be, likewise, inactive. The reason is that inorganic things are composed of matter and form. Nevertheless, *de facto*, Aristotle regarded inorganic reality as inactive. He was convinced that inorganic reality, because of the forms embodied in it, contained a principle enabling it to be specifically moved but not a principle of specific active movement. This Aristotelian idea was taken over by the Middle Ages, notably by Thomas Aquinas. It is a point of great importance, especially in connection with the prominent position assigned to finality in the Aristotelian and Thomistic world view.

Following Aristotle, Thomas thought that the specifically different ways of acting and reacting proper to the various inorganic materials could not be sufficiently explained through elementary qualities, such as heat. For the same agent, heat, produces a variety of forms. Therefore, a more powerful agent must play a role when heat acts, and this agent belongs to the realm of "celestial bodies."[7] Because the nature of material things (understood as "sublunary" bodies) is a principle of being moved rather than of active movement, they need to be influenced by the stars and planets. "Celestial bodies," it should be recalled, were also regarded as composed of matter and form, but in such a way that they were subject only to local motion. Their matter was of a higher and more noble kind than terrestrial matter, for the latter is also the principle that subjects earthly things to coming to be and passing away, something to which celestial bodies are not subject.

Of course, the mere capacity for local motion, even for "perfect" circular motion,[8] was not sufficient to explain the causal influence exercised by celestial bodies on terrestrial events. Something else was needed, and this could only be something spiritual. Since terrestrial motions were clearly ordered to an end, there had to be a spiritual intelligence to explain this purposive character. In this way, the

---

[7]*Summa theologica,* p. I, q. 115, a.3, *ad* 2.
[8]Circular motion was "perfect" because it did not have a beginning or an end.

next step that naturally suggested itself was to connect intelligences
with the celestial bodies, which were already regarded as much more
perfect than terrestrial bodies.

Although Thomas Aquinas was very uncertain about the way in
which intelligences were connected with the stars, he did not doubt
that there was a connection.[9] For, the finality of all terrestrial events
could be explained only if celestial bodies and their causal action
on terrestrial events were influenced by beings endowed with intelligence.[10] The statement that all motion on earth tended to an
end was regarded as certain, for the various terrestrial elements tended
to their "natural place" as their end. With respect to earth and water,
this tendency gave rise to a downward motion, a motion of falling;
hence these elements were "heavy." In air and fire it gave rise to an
upward motion because their natural place was above the earth. Accordingly, although terrestrial bodies lacked intellectual knowledge
or animal instinct, they could act with finality or design because their
action was directed by the causality of celestial bodies which possessed
purposiveness through their connection with intelligences.

It is hardly necessary to point out that, in these Greek and medieval
views about matter, both philosophical ideas and primitive scientific
notions played a role. The fact that Aristotle and Thomas Aquinas
explicitly appealed to celestial bodies and their intelligences to explain
the specific actions of terrestrial bodies has to be attributed, of course,
to the complete absence of any scientific theories that could explain
these specific actions. They likewise lacked the necessary data to assign
an adequate terrestrial cause to the order resulting from these actions.
For this reason they were induced to overemphasize finality in their
reflections upon these questions.

At the same time, however, the view that matter is the principle of
mutability and of individual realization possessed a philosophical depth
which penetrates into much more fundamental structures of reality
than those that were explicitly raised in the then current world view.
Of particular interest is that hylomorphism, as the Aristotelian theory
of matter and form is called, led to the conclusion that material reality
is fundamentally changeable. Because prime matter has no deter-

---

[9]*Contra Gentiles,* bk. III, ch. 23.

[10]Hence, it is certainly incorrect to regard the ancient view of the influence
exercised by the sun on terrestrial events as a primitive predecessor of the
contemporary scientific view of the sun as a source of energy. Such a benev-
olent interpretation is sometimes made, but is not in agreement with the facts.
Cf. Raymond J. Nogar, "Evolution: Scientific and Philosophical Dimensions,"
Philosophy of Biology, ed. by Vincent E. Smith, New York, 1962, p. 59.

minations whatsoever in itself but is in principle capable of all determinations, any concrete material being is subject to being changed into any other concrete material being. This radical mutability, however, must not be misunderstood. It does not mean that arbitrariness governs the material world. The fundamental mutability remains encompassed by a fixed order.

Strange as it may seem, the Aristotelian view remains valid even in the context of an evolutionary world view. This is a sign of its philosophical depth, for it was not primarily concerned with the possibility of such a world picture. While it would be going too far to claim that the evolutionary perspective was entirely absent from Greek thought,[11] this perspective was certainly not predominant, especially not in Aristotle.

For Aristotle the radical mutability of matter was concerned with concrete material beings but not with the total order of material reality. These concrete beings could come to be from other concrete beings and pass away into them, but the same forms were constantly being realized in them. We may note here that the same idea still lies at the foundation of contemporary physical science. In a chemical reaction, for instance, water is realized from hydrogen and oxygen. This concrete water can be transformed into other combinations. In other words, water, hydrogen and oxygen are not "eternal" in their concrete realizations, but only in their structures, for these structures—"forms" in Aristotelian terms—of water, hydrogen and oxygen are constantly actualized. There is, as it were, a fixed supply of possible forms in the material world, and these forms are there either actually or potentially.

The modern view differs from the Aristotelian conception in that contemporary chemistry proceeds from the conviction that many more structures are possible than those which have ever been actualized by nature. These structures are, as it were, waiting for man. Modern chemistry, therefore, makes no difference between structures realized by nature and structures realized by man. Both are equally "natural." True, the modern chemist performs feats of molecule-engineering, but even then it is always a question of realizing the potentialities of nature. Moreover, even with respect to these new forms, once they are discovered, the chemist can produce or

---

[11]Cf. W. Zimmermann, *Evolution, die Geschichte ihrer Probleme und Erkenntnisse*, Freiburg i. Br., 2nd ed., 1954.

destroy their concrete realizations as he wants. In other words, the fundamental idea of Aristotle's conception remains valid.

Similar considerations also apply to the realm of life. Here too, according to Aristotle, concrete reality consists of individual realizations of a "fixed supply" of forms. Here too, however, science has discovered that stability is supplemented by the possibility of a development through which the actually existing order of forms is being modified, has been modified in the past, and will be modified in the future. Daring speculations assume that the range of these modifications is so vast that at one time the living forms were purely potential and merely contained as future possibilities in the actually existing inorganic chemical structures.

The radical possibility of change presupposed by the theory of evolution was entirely unknown to Aristotle. He was acquainted with so-called spontaneous generation, the passage from the inorganic to the living; but this transition was encompassed by the constantly recurring cycle of events. Although, nearly always, living beings came from other living beings of the same kind, there were a few constantly recurring exceptions. Eels, for example, Aristotle held, originated from mud. These exceptions, however, had nothing to do with evolution. Spontaneous generation had its place in a static world view. This world view was not static in the sense that it did not know radical mutability, but in the sense that, no matter what radical changes individual beings underwent, the cosmic order in its totality remained as it was.

Nevertheless, it remains true that hylomorphism, with its theory of the radical mutability of material reality, contained a dynamism which went far beyond the static world view that had witnessed its birth. It was this dynamism which, coupled with that of Democritus' atomistic theory of active atoms, laid the foundations of the future physical science.

Surveying the entire period of the Greeks and the Middle Ages, we find there the following conceptions about matter:

1. Matter as a relative concept, in opposition to matter as the concrete material being itself (Aristotle in opposition to Democritus);

2. Matter as the aspect that limits and resists form, idea and spirit, in opposition to matter as the basis of all activity (Plato and Aristotle in opposition to Democritus);

3. Terrestrial matter in opposition to the matter of celestial bodies.

3. THE NEW ERA

Because philosophical ideas and primitive scientific conceptions intermingled in man's thinking about matter, the rise of physical science was bound to cause an upheaval in the more or less petrified positions of antiquity and the Middle Ages. First of all, the distinction between celestial matter and terrestrial matter had to be dropped. The movements of celestial bodies are governed by the same mechanics as those of terrestrial bodies. Hence there was no longer any reason to assign a higher ontological status to celestial bodies. Consequently, there could be no question of maintaining the view that the order of terrestrial events is brought about by "intelligences." Likewise, there was no longer any room in the explanation of nature for a causal finality conceived in direct analogy with human activity. Qualities and forces that explain the phenomena of nature were now ascribed to matter itself. Bodies were regarded as having an activity of their own, and this activity was given a place in the scheme of mechanism. Through the work of Gassendi, Democritus became the center of attention, sharing the limelight with Descartes, the great philosopher of the new era.

Democritus and Descartes together determined man's thinking about matter in the seventeenth century. In a sense this was rather strange because there were striking differences between their views. For Descartes matter was *res extensa,* extended reality, in opposition to *res cogitans,* spirit or reality without extension. But if matter is identical with extension, atomism is in theory untenable, since the extended is divisible to infinity. For this reason Descartes resolutely rejected atomism. This rejection, however, did not prevent him from developing a kind of corpuscular theory,[12] in which a function was assigned to particles characterized by a determined state of motion. Precisely this emphasis on the state of motion brought Democritus and Descartes together in the eyes of the latter's contemporaries, because this emphasis drew attention to mechanics. The theory of mechanics, which had been developed to explain the motion of celestial bodies and earthly objects, was now extended to the assumed motions of corpuscles. Thus it became necessary to assign properties to them

---

[12]Cf. A. G. van Melsen, *From Atomos to Atom. The History of the Concept "Atom,"* Pittsburgh, 1952, ch. III, section 5. For more details concerning the historical explanations presented here we refer the reader to this work.

which had a place in physics, such as mass, and properties which were chemically relevant, such as a specific chemical activity.

However, it is not correct to claim, as is often done, that the seventeenth century's greatest merit lies in the revival of the corpuscular theory. What this century did was to connect the corpuscular theory with the new-born physical science, thereby giving rise to an atomic concept that could be physically and chemically fruitful. The corpuscular theory itself had never died in the Middle Ages, but had always continued to exist, even in Aristotelian circles in the form of the "minima naturalia" theory. This theory started with the assumption that the division of a particular kind of matter could never be continued to infinity because there existed natural minima for every kind of matter, whether elementary or composite. Below that minimum the form could no longer be realized. In the course of centuries, this theory underwent an important development: the natural minima, originally the ultimate limits of division within which the form could still be realized, came to be seen as the building blocks of material reality. This development had been started by Aristotle's Greek Commentators, but its major impetus had come from the Averroists.

The strong point of this theory lay in the fact that it knew specific minima for every material being, for elements and compounds as well as for living beings. Its weakness was that it seemed intrinsically connected with the theory of four elements, and this theory offered no prospect of leading to physically and chemically useful concepts that would characterize the minima. Such a prospect, however, was offered by the new mechanics of the seventeenth century. For the same reason the seventeenth century was not satisfied with the revived atomism of Democritus and its atoms infinitely varied, but differing only in size and shape, for such atoms, like the "minima naturalia," were unable to explain the specific reactions of the various kinds of material being. For this reason Gassendi spoke not only of atoms but also of molecules, that is, composite atoms. When water evaporates it is not dissolved into atoms but into molecules composed of atoms. Hence the vapor can return easily to water. Nevertheless, atoms remained of chief importance for Gassendi.

Boyle, however, took a different view. He called the composite atoms "primary concretions." For every kind of matter, these primary concretions were different. And, although they were composed of atoms, they never decomposed. Boyle regarded these concretions as the true building blocks of nature, which could be united to form concretions of a higher order. His theory prepared the way for Dalton's concept of the atom which admitted, for every chemical element, distinct atoms endowed with specifically different natures. Dalton was already so attuned to physical science that he no longer felt any need to express the purely theoretical adherence to Democritus which is still to be found in Boyle.

Beginning with the seventeenth century, man's explicit thinking about matter was strongly influenced by mechanism, especially in its atomistic variation. At the same time, however, it was also controlled by the inherent demands of the new physical science. The result was that purity of doctrine became a matter of secondary importance. Hence, if one wants to evaluate the thought of the new era about matter, it is absolutely necessary to make a distinction between physical science's implicit concept of matter and, on the other hand, the explicit concept.

In line with the remarks made in the preceding chapter about the relationship between philosophy and physical science, the term "implicit concept of matter" refers to that view of matter which is implied by, and at the foundation of, the method of physical science. For obvious reasons it is not easy to explicitate and describe this implicit concept of matter. We will therefore enumerate a few points that are important for a confrontation of the implicit concept with the explicit concept and for an understanding of the subsequent development of physical science. These few points, however, will prove highly interesting, especially when compared with the explicit concepts of matter proposed by Gassendi, Descartes, Boyle, Dalton and others.

These points are the following:

1. Physical science starts from the assumption that everything material, including living beings and man himself insofar as he is material, possesses a repeatable structure. Any concrete being, any property and any event can be analyzed in terms of magnitudes that occur constantly and realize themselves over and over. It is not difficult to recognize here a fundamental idea of Aristotle that we have pointed out above: every concrete reality is the materialization of certain specificities or rather of a complex of specificities.

2. We say "complex," because physical science also proceeds from the assumption that the above-mentioned specificities are

interconnected. For, while approaching every concrete being analytically, physical science knows that the occurrence of these specificities alongside one another is not purely arbitrary. They always occur in certain complexes. Iron, for example, is always characterized by a certain interconnected whole of specific properties. Along with these properties, any concrete realization of iron also has a number of variable qualities. In addition to certain physical and chemical properties shared with all iron, a piece of iron has accidental qualities, such as a particular degree of temperature.

3. The various specificities and their complexes exhibit a certain order. This order makes it possible to explain one complex by means of another. The structure, for example, of the iron atom explains the various chemical properties that are of necessity, i.e., according to certain laws, connected with this structure. At the same time, it explains the possible presence of other qualities that need not be there *per se,* but whose occurrence also is governed by laws.

The fundamental idea of this reducibility is found as early as Democritus, who wanted to reduce all properties to atoms and their configurations. In this he differed from Aristotle, for whom an appeal to the nature of the thing in question was, strictly speaking, the last word, because he felt that in reality many irreducible natures existed alongside one another. The ultimate significance of the confidence in the reducibility of properties appears to lie in its basic view that there is only one material reality, only one nature.

4. Physical science also starts from an assumption which we may call a general law of the conservation of matter and all its fundamental properties. There is in short, no creation from nothing nor annihilation. Whatever manifests itself at any given moment and was not before must have been potentially contained in something else. Its appearance, then, may be new, but it must find its explanation in that which was already.

5. Matter itself is active. Any activity occurring in the material world must find its explanation in this world and not outside it. Causality, therefore, is not merely the aspect of deterministic reality spoken of in Points Three and Four, but

also involves real activity. This activity, moreover, makes matter knowable to us.

6. Matter has a qualitative-quantitative structure, in the sense that all material events must be both sense perceptible and capable of mathematical description. Such a structure is required in order that measurement can be the typical way of perceiving proper to physical science.

7. Physical science assumes that all the concrete things it studies are radically changeable. For whatever is not subject to change would be beyond experimental verification and, consequently, would not be knowable by physical science.

These points do not summarize the *results* of scientific research concerning matter but rather a view of matter that makes the research of physical science possible. Experimentation is meaningful only with respect to a reality exhibiting the above-mentioned characteristics. Let us illustrate this matter briefly.

If there were no structure of repeatability (Point One) revealing itself in analysis, induction and *a fortiori* experimentation would be impossible. For, obviously, the varying of different factors would be meaningless if the same processes could not be repeated. There would be no connection between successive experiments. The presupposition of laws governing material reality (Points Two and Three) is based upon the same ground.

Experimental research would likewise be meaningless if there were creation from nothing, that is, if phenomena occurred without any bond with preceding phenomena (Point Four). For the same reason all material activities encountered in matter must be activities of matter itself, for experimental science would not be able to deal with preternatural agencies. It is in the reaction imposed on matter by the experiment that matter makes itself known (Point Five). The fact that matter lets itself be known through measurement (Point Six) indicates that the quantitative element and the qualitative element do not exist alongside each other as experience at first seems to say, but constitute together a single structure: hence the perceptible is the measurable, and the measurable is the perceptible.

Finally, the idea that material reality lets itself be known only experimentally presupposes that material reality does not contain any entities that are, in principle, not subject to change. Only that which can be changed is subject to experimentation.

If we compare this implicit concept of matter with the explicit concept prevailing in the seventeenth century, it is striking to note that this explicit concept, despite its variations in different thinkers, was much more limited and much less rich in content than the implicit concept.

The infinitely varied atoms of Democritus' atomism made the repeatable structure of matter a mere illusion, and for this reason Boyle and Dalton resorted to specifically distinct atoms. But this was much too limited, at least in Dalton, who retained the idea that the atoms were immutable. The great weakness of the mechanistic concept of matter, with its essentially immutable atoms, was that it forced man's analyzing experiments to stop at the atoms, since any further research would have been impossible (cf. Point Seven). This impossibility, however, could only then be of no consequence if the atoms themselves somehow were perfectly known. Mechanism, by holding this view, revealed its essentially rationalistic origin. For Descartes, matter, at least as he conceived it, was like a "clear and distinct idea," so that any further investigation was superfluous. All this, however, contradicts the empirical-experimental character of physical science which is never finished, not even with regard to our knowledge of any of its "parts."

Mechanism provided an intolerable restriction with respect to the general law of conservation of matter (Point Four) and the active character of matter (Point Five). By holding that in all processes the atoms were retained with their figure, size and mass, and by reducing all activities to these magnitudes, mechanism set up a demand that could hardly be satisfied by the concept of mass as it was then conceived. Consequently, in practice the scientists of the time did not follow this requirement of mechanism. Dalton, for example, attributed all kinds of distinct chemical properties to his atoms.

Another interesting point in this connection is that mechanism, while correctly emphasizing the quantitative aspect of matter, recognized only size and figure as quantitative aspects (cf. Point Six). As a result of this restriction, it did not go beyond those aspects which were immediately given and thus became unable to pay attention to the much more fundamental aspects of the quantitative structure.

In conclusion, let us point out that, although seventeenth century physical science managed to abolish the dichotomy between celestial and terrestrial matter, it was confronted with a new dichotomy, viz., that between corpuscular matter and its phenomena, on the one hand, and the ether and its phenomena of light, on the other. Because the predominant mechanistic view equated matter with mass, the strange custom arose of referring to the phenomena in the ether as "immaterial."[13] Even today there remain traces of this mechanistic influence. For example, the change of elementary particles into radiation phenomena is referred to as "dematerialization," as if the latter were no longer material. Yet their materiality is attested to by the fact that they are subject to the same experimental method of research that aims at knowledge of the material world.

Accordingly, the explicit concept of matter, with its mechanistic framework, its thesis of immutable material beings in the form of particles, and its distinction between ponderable matter and immaterial physical phenomena, differed considerably from the implicit concept of matter on which the method of physical science was based and which was much more subtle and richer in possibilities. In the first stage of physical science this discrepancy did not appear too serious because it seemed that the deviations from the mechanistic ideal, such as ascribing specific properties to atoms, were merely of a provisional nature. As physical science developed, however, the inner consequences of the implicit concept of the matter were bound to become increasingly clearer and reveal that the mechanistic concept was no longer tenable.

The reason why this happened becomes clear when we notice the characteristics of the development undergone by physical science. First of all, the experimental character of this science, and all its implications, became the center of attention much more than they had been in the first phase of physical science. Secondly, the unity of everything material manifested itself more clearly than ever. The "sectors" of material reality covered, on the one hand, by the wave theory and, on the other, by the corpuscular theory merged into a single complex. There is now no longer any room for "immaterial" phenomena alongside material phenomena. Thirdly, it became evident that all material entities are radically changeable, and this fact opened immense new possibilities for the study of the "building blocks" of

---

[13] *Grimsehls Lehrbuch der Physik,* revised by R. Tomaschek, vol. 2, Leipzig, 10th ed., 1942, p. 287, a well-known text, called even the electron "immaterial," because the term "matter" was explicitly connected with things composed of atoms.

matter. Finally, all this gave greater emphasis than ever before to
the progressive character of physical science. Today physical science
is more convinced than ever that its achievements constitute only
the first feeble beginning of the unimaginable program of the future.
Yet, unlike the suggestions of nineteenth century physical science,
it does not feel that the elementary building blocks of matter are
already known and that, hence, its program can *de facto* be limited
to reducing all macro-phenomena, including those of the biological
realm, to man's acquired knowledge of these building blocks. For
better knowledge of any complex leads physical science to new knowledge about its building blocks and vice versa, in an unending
interaction.

The mechanistic concept of matter was not merely exposed to the
internal critique necessitated by the development of physical science,
but it possessed sufficient philosophical aspects to be the object of a
more or less independent philosophical critique. A critical thinker
like Kant could hardly be satisfied with the naive realism that identified the mechanistic world view with reality itself. He especially dis-
trusted the fact that the mechanistic view relied so strongly on sense
intuition, which was precisely its point of greatest appeal. In
his critique he argued that this reliance led to all kinds of
contradictions.[14]

Moreover, man's constructive work functioned as the model of
mechanism, for its very name refers to "mechanics," which originally
meant "skill in making tools and instruments." It conceived the
reality of nature as analogous to a mechanical construction. In a
certain sense therefore mechanism was based on a procedure similar
to Aristotle's physics. Aristotle's doctrine of the four causes, the
material, the formal, the efficient and the final cause, was derived
from the work done by a craftsman. A mechanic was merely a more
up to date version of the old craftsman and not essentially different.
Both had to select their materials and give them a form that would
bring about the desired end. Aristotle thought that the same four
causes would serve to explain the events of nature. Kant was more
critical, but his critique did not attack the procedure as such, i.e.,
conceiving nature by way of analogy with human constructions.[15]

---

[14]*Kritik der reinen Vernunft*, Elementarlehre, Zweiter Teil, Zweite Abteil-
ung, Zweites Buch, 2. Hauptstück, 2. Abschnitt. In the *Philos. Bibliothek* ed.,
vol. 37a, Hamburg, 1952, pp. 448 ff.
[15]Cf. K. Kuypers, *Wetenschap en kunde*, Utrecht, 1951, pp. 12 ff.

As Kant tells us in his *Kritik der Urteilskraft,* in studying nature we must pay attention to that "which we can subject to our observation or experiments in such a way that we ourselves can produce it like nature, at least according to the similarity of the laws. For one fully understands only as much as one can personally make or produce."[16] Kant's critique, then, was not directed against the mechanistic procedure but against something else, namely, the question whether knowledge construed in such a fashion could reach reality itself. Keeping in mind that in his time man's cognitive grasp and technical grip had not yet merged, this critique was bound to arise. For, as we have seen, since Aristotle technique and science had gone their separate ways; technical knowledge was precisely not a science, even though it had undoubtedly rendered service to the rise and development of science.

When Kant wrote his *Critique of Pure Reason,* he had in mind Newton's physical science and the cognitive possibilities it disclosed. Although Newton's science used the senses more intensely than ever before in the acquisition and verification of knowledge, it still remained a largely theoretical science. We may add in passing that astronomy is only now beginning to lose this purely theoretical charactertistic. Thus, when Kant in his *Critique of Practical Reason* devoted attention to human activity and its ethical dimensions but neglected technique, it was typical of his era. For scientific technique hardly existed then. For Kant, therefore, there was a great discrepancy between man's theoretical or cognitive grasp and his operational or technical grip on things. Man was able to picture nature as a mechanism and even had to picture it in such a way, but if nature were a mechanism, why did it not slide easily under man's technical grip? Could nature be a mechanism if man's technical grip lagged so far behind his cognitive grasp? This question almost inevitably gave rise to the epistemological problem regarding the subjective character of the imagination and man's cognitive categories. Obviously, in this respect the present development of physical science forces us to raise the epistemological problem in a new way.

We will revert to this point later in connection with the problem of causality. At present we are mainly concerned with the conse-

---

[16] *Kritik der Urteilskraft,* par. 68: ". . . was wir unserer Beobachtung oder Experimenten so unterwerfen können, dasz wir es gleich der Natur, wenigstens der Ahnlichkeit der Gesetze nach, selbst herforbringen könnten; denn nur soviel sieht man volständig ein, als man selbst machen und zustande bringen kann."

quences Kant's critique had for the concept of matter. Paradoxically, this critique invalidated the mechanistic way of thinking and at the same time canonized it. By unmasking this way of thinking as a subjective mode of considering reality, the critique invalidated mechanism and, at the same time, canonized it by declaring that this subjective way of thinking was the only possible way, the way directly imposed upon man by his cognitive structure. For us the important point is that, under the influence of Kant, there arose a concept of matter which no longer referred directly to material reality but functioned as the correlate of the scientific approach to reality. According to this view, man could conceive matter only in the categories of mechanism. This explicit concept of matter resulted from Kant's contribution to philosophy.

Reflecting on the concept of matter proper to the new era, we notice the importance of the distinction that manifested itself in this time between the implicit and the explicit concepts of matter. For, as we have seen, the implicit concept that is at work in physical science is much richer and more flexible than its actual explicitations. This statement applies not only to the explicitations preceding the birth of physical science, such as those of Democritus, Plato, Aristotle and Thomas Aquinas, but also to those made under the influence of physical science itself, such as the views of mechanism then in vogue among scientists and Kant's reaction to it. The limited value of these explicitations was the reason why they were constantly overtaken by the development of physical science.

All this shows that material reality, the object of physical science, is richer than any explicit scientific or philosophical view. This is hardly surprising if we keep in mind that human knowledge is limited and that physical science has a progressive nature. At the same time, however, this points to something really surprising, namely, the fact that the implicit view of physical science contains a virtual wealth which can hardly be expressed in any other terms than by saying that somehow physical science shares in the infinite wealth of being proper to human knowing. We do not merely mean that man's knowing is open to this wealth of being, but also that this wealth is to some extent already possessed by man by virtue of his mode of being, by virtue of the fact that man is a knowing being.

It is true, of course, that physical science shares only in a limited way in this wealth of being; but it has a particularly privileged share. This privileged status is probably connected with the typically progressive character of physical science mentioned in the first chapter. An original impulse is at work in physical science. And although this impulse has found a focal point, and consequently also a limitation, in the specific way in which science approaches reality, this impulse appears to contain a wealth of being that constantly opens up on much broader horizons than one would at first suspect. Not only is this implicit view of material reality virtually richer than any of the explicit positions of physical science and the corresponding philosophical explicitations, but it appears to contain also a virtually much richer view of man himself; for this vision reveals itself in a clearer way only gradually as physical science advances in its development.

If these ideas are true, it is not surprising that physical science has contributed in an extraordinary way to giving man a clearer understanding of living reality. We will devote the following chapter to this question.

CHAPTER FOUR

LIFE

1. The Problem of Life

Prescientific experience assigns a special place to living beings among the many shapes and forms exhibited by the reality of nature. Scientific experience concurs with this distinction and has contributed in many direct and indirect ways to clarifying the basis of this distinction. The simple fact that biology itself occupies a special position among the sciences of nature indicates sufficiently how much this science realizes the special character of the material reality with which it deals. Biology is aware that this special character is not found everywhere in the material world and refers to it as "life."

It is striking that, when the biologist tries to describe this special character, he appeals to characteristics known from prescientific experience of living beings. Any characterization of life refers explicitly or implicitly to concepts such as self-movement, nutrition, growth, and reproduction, which were already mentioned by Aristotle in his well-known treatise on life.[1] Strange as it may seem, although biology knows much about life, it never completely manages to define life conceptually in such a way that the living is unambiguously divided from the non-living.

The question arising spontaneously in connection with this lack of an unambiguous definition is whether the failure is caused by the means man has to arrive at explicit knowledge of life or by the fact that in reality there is no sharp distinction between the living and the non-living. This question in its turn raises another question, viz., whether or not the answer can be found without taking into consideration the development of physical science, and particularly of biology. In other words, here again we meet the implicit view of life that is active in biology and which assumes a clearer form only in and through the development of this science. This implicit view embodies an original experience of being, in the sense discussed at the end of the preceding chapter. The presence of such an experience

---

[1] *De anima*, bk. II, ch. 4. English text in W. D. Ross, *The Works of Aristotle*, vol. 3, tr. by J. A. Smith. This treatise remains eminently worthwhile reading.

manifests itself very clearly in biology. In attempting to describe the subject matter of his science, the biologist often sees himself forced to appeal to the concept of life as it is known to man from his self-experience. This self-experience is nothing but man's "lived" self-presence.

Some biologists do not hesitate to make that appeal rather openly For example, A. Portmann writes: "Accordingly, living beings appear to us as patterned wholes (*Gestalten*) which change their form in conformity with certain laws through growth and assimilation; they appear to us as patterned wholes which overcome their corruptibility through reproduction and hereditary transmission; and finally as wholes which all, be it in very different ways, are capable of relatively autonomous activity. A very special condition of life manifests itself in this activity, which condition we have called 'interiority'."[2]

Other biologists are not inclined to include interiority in their description or definition of life.[3] There are several reasons for their reluctance. First of all, there is an objection with respect to the content of such a definition, precisely because interiority appeals to phenomena of consciousness which man experiences in himself. While there may be reasons in favor of admitting such phenomena not only in man but also in higher forms of animal life, plants reveal no sign of consciousness. Consequently, interiority does not seem to be characteristic of all life but belongs only to some of the forms of being which the biologist calls "life."

One who simply and unqualifiedly connects life with interiority seems to forget that life is not a univocal concept. For the concept of life is used to characterize not only vegetative life but also sensitive life and human life, and this broader use of the concept is not limited to certain biological characteristics that these three forms of life have in common, such as metabolism, growth and reproduction. If

---

[2]*Probleme des Lebens,* Basel, 1949, p. 16: "Die Lebewesen sind uns also erschienen als Gestalten mit gesetzmäsziger Formwandlung, einer Formwandlung, welche durch Wachstum und durch Stoffwechsel geschieht, als Gestalten, die ihre Hinfälligkeit überwinden durch Fortpflanzung und Vererbung, und schlieszlich als Gestalten, die alle, wenn auch in sehr verschiedenem Grade, zu relativ selbständigem Tun fähig sind, in dem sich ein ganz besonderer Zustand des Lebens äuszert, den wir die Innerlichkeit genannt haben."

[3]L. von Bertalanffy may be quoted as an example. He arrives at the following definition of life: "A living organism is a hierarchical order of open systems which maintains itself in the exchange of components by virtue of its system conditions" (*Problems of Life,* New York, 1952, p. 129). This definition shows a desire to remain as close as possible to a description in terms of physical science, even at the risk that certain ingeniously devised artifacts may satisfy the definition.

this limitation existed with respect to the use of the concept "life," one could argue perhaps that this concept is univocal. But we use the same concept "life" also in "the life of the spirit," for example; and in this expression the term is given a meaning which is typically different from the sense in which the biologist speaks of life. Precisely because interiority characterizes the life of the spirit, with its self-presence and self-reflection, it seems to be improper to appeal to interiority when one wants to define biological life.

Moreover, even on methodological grounds, many will reject any reference to interiority because biology is a physical science. Interiority as such is not subject to the cognitive possibilities open to physical science, for this science has as its object only that which can be registered by means of external perception.

Although these two arguments appear rather impressive, they are not entirely satisfactory. If by virtue of its methodic approach physical science knows nothing about interiority, this does not mean much with respect to the absence or presence of this interiority. At most, such methodological considerations would permit us to conclude that it is not the task of biology as a physical science to present an explicit definition of life—just as physical science likewise abstains from defining matter explicitly. At any rate, the argument does not allow us to conclude that interiority may not be included in the definition of life.

Let us now investigate the other argument, which points out that the phenomena of consciousness are not characteristic of life in all its forms. While this statement can hardly be denied, these phenomena, nonetheless, are so intimately connected with the material structure of living beings that it is difficult to regard them as external additions rather than as an unfolding of something which is given in capacity in every form of life. These phenomena appear to have something to do with a more or less pronounced emergence of a "self." Such a "self" offers at least its first manifestations in any form of life, as is implied in the classical descriptions of life as self-development and self-movement. Despite their age, these classical definitions retain their illuminating character.

What is the nature of this "self"? Is it strictly special to life, something that manifests itself only in the realm of life, be it in different degrees of intensity; or should the specific element of life be sought rather in a special organization of matter? These questions put us squarely in the middle of the old dispute between vitalism and mechanism. The history of this dispute is very instructive, not only with respect to the relationship between living and non-living but also with reference to the competence of physical science to speak about the difference between living and non-living. Hence we will first consider this dispute and then return to the question of interiority and the proper character of life.

2. VITALISM AND MECHANISM

The center of the dispute between vitalism and mechanism is whether life must be considered a higher form of being than the non-living, purely material being. As early as the controversy between Aristotle and Democritus, we see the beginnings of this dispute. For Democritus there was no question of an essential difference between living and non-living beings; they differed only in their atomic configuration. Aristotle, on the other hand, left room for an essential difference in his theory of matter and form. Although, according to Aristotle, both living and non-living beings were composed of matter and form, the form of the living being essentially differed from that of the nonliving being. Aristotle sought this difference in the power or principle of self-movement, which characterized everything living.

For a correct evaluation of this characteristic one should keep in mind that, according to Aristotle, non-living beings are always moved from without. As we noted in a preceding chapter, Aristotle's criterion in this matter could not be maintained in the light of subsequent discoveries made by physical science, at least not in the way he presented his criterion, on the basis of a primitive experience. From the standpoint of primitive experience, the matter is perfectly clear. A simple observation shows whether or not a material being is living: a non-living being does not move "of itself," but a living being does.

Physical science, however, has discovered how much an apparently unmoved thing, that is, an inorganic being in a state of rest, is constantly in restless and dynamic inner "movement." This movement does not necessarily have to be motion in the sense of mechanism. True, the first theories about the atom's composition conceived its inner dynamism as the motion of electrons orbiting around a nucleus and as "leaps" from one shell to another—in other words, as pure locomotion. The critique which quantum mechanics made of this view, however, was not addressed to the dynamism in question but only its mechanical model, or rather to the fact that this model was supposed to represent reality unqualifiedly. There can be no doubt at all that the atom is full of "self-movement" and that atoms are constantly acting on one another. Nevertheless, no one will see a reason here to call atoms, and inorganic things composed of atoms in a natural or in an artificial way, "living beings." Artifacts especially can possess a large measure of self-movement, as is indicated by the term "automobile." Perhaps we may add that the strange etymology of this term, which borrows its first part from the Greek *autos,* self, and the second from the Latin *mobilis,* movable, could be interpreted as a sign that its inventors had tongue in cheek when they called the contraption an "automobile." Anyhow, even artificial "self-movers" of far greater perfection than the automobile continue to be regarded as essentially different from living beings.

Strange as it may seem, further reflection on the difference between technical "self-movers" and living beings again draws attention to Aristotle's original criterion. Regardless of philosophical considerations, we may observe that technical "self-movers" receive their principle of self-movement from without, through human ingenuity, while living beings have this principle from within. Hardly anyone, we think, will be inclined to disagree with this statement. Disagreement, however, begins as soon as one asks what this inner principle is. Is this principle nothing but a continuation of the atom's own possibilities—possibilities which develop in the macro-structures formed from the atoms and which, by virtue of the complexities of these structures, manifest the specific phenomena of life? Or does all life have a specific principle that cannot be reduced to inorganic microstructures? Vitalism argues in favor of the second view, mechanism in favor of the first, and both views adduce impressive arguments for their conviction.

The arguments in question have frequently been modified, and the reason is not difficult to see. As should be evident from the preceding pages, the dispute between vitalism and mechanism has two aspects. On the one hand, it is based on fundamentally different philosophical views on the nature of living beings, and these views have managed to maintain themselves throughout history. On the other, the dispute is permeated with all kinds of scientific ideas, which have undergone many changes in the course of time. Because of these changes, the criterion of self-movement can no longer be handled in the same way as it was in the time of Aristotle, even though the criterion itself continues to retain its actual value, at least with respect to formulating the problem.

Although the controversy between vitalism and mechanism is very old as a philosophical dispute, it became an especially acute question when within biology itself there appeared possibilities of arriving effectively at scientific explanations. These possibilities manifested themselves only in modern times, as is evident from the term "mechanism" itself, even though the fundamental meaning of this term goes back to the birth of classical physical science. "Mechanism" expresses the conviction that all phenomena, no matter how complicated, can ultimately be understood in terms of the mechanical properties of matter. These properties are studied by the science of mechanics, which initially functioned as the universal science of nature.

In biology mechanism had at first the same meaning. When, however, mechanical models showed their insufficiency in physics, a somewhat different sense of mechanism began to prevail in biology. It assumed the form of the statement that all phenomena of life can be explained in a physico-chemical fashion. The reason for this modification was rather obvious. In the context of biology the important point in the dispute between mechanism and vitalism was whether or not the phenomena of living nature could be explained in the same way as those of non-living nature. From the standpoint of biology it did not matter whether the development of chemistry and physics forced these sciences to make use of non-mechanical models. That issue had to be decided by chemistry and physics but not by biology.

Mechanism is also known as materialism and causalism. Both terms again indicate a slight shift in meaning, a different accent. The use of the term "materialism" emphasizes that all phenomena of life must be explained in terms of the fundamental properties of matter; in other words, life is nothing but a particular structure of matter. The term "causalism," on the other hand, draws attention to the fact that even the most complex phenomena of life with their seeming purposiveness can be fully explained in terms of the causal actions of the elementary particles whose self-activity had been discovered by classical physical science.

Vitalism goes counter to these views, which, despite their differences, are intimately connected because they flow from the same fundamental conception. According to vitalism, a special principle is at work in life. This principle, which is variously known as *vis vitalis,* "entelechy," "soul" and *élan vital,* to name only a few terms, regulates the vital operations and attunes them to the purpose of life from the standpoint of the individual or that of the species. For this reason vitalism is also known as "finalism." And because the principle of life was often regarded as non-material, vitalism was also viewed as the opposite of materialism.

All these differentiations show that the opposition between mechanism and vitalism is concerned with several issues which, despite their connection, are not at all identical. The history of the dispute clearly confirms this statement. In many respects this history has also thrown clarity on methodical matters; or, to express it in line with the discussion about the relationship between philosophy and physical science (Chapter Two), through the progress in biology we now know better what this science tacitly but methodically presupposes about life and matter. For this reason it is useful to discuss briefly a few points from the history of biology that are of importance for the controversy between mechanism and vitalism.

One of the first problems in this history was spontaneous generation, the question whether, by way of exception to the general rules, some species of living beings are spontaneously generated from non-living matter. As we have mentioned, in ancient and medieval times this question was generally answered in the affirmative. Experience seemed to teach it, for one could see living beings arise from putrified flesh. Materialistic conclusions, however, were not considered necessarily connected with spontaneous generation, as appears from the fact that it was accepted by such thinkers as Aristotle, Augustine and Thomas Aquinas, whose ideas were vitalistic rather than mechanistic. These philosophers did not base their acceptance on the forces of inorganic matter itself but on the causal influence of the sun or of the Creator.

With the rise of physical science in the seventeenth century, spontaneous generation became a topic of experimental research, which before long became centered on the question of the spontaneous generation of *infusoria.* Pasteur's experiments finally removed all reasonable doubt in 1862. He was able to show that even the smallest living beings were generated from other living beings and not from non-living matter. There seemed to be an unbridgeable gap between living and non-living matter.

Nevertheless, in the middle of the nineteenth century, proponents of evolution postulated the origin of life from non-living matter. This postulate appeared to be an unjustified, and consequently unscientific, extrapolation of the idea of evolution. Fruitful as the idea of evolution could be within the realm of the living, there was not a single specific argument on which one could base its extension from the living to the non-living. The true reason for the extrapolation seemed to lie in the rejection of the idea of creation. In this way the controversy between vitalism and mechanism acquired again another aspect. Mechanism now seemed to be identical with atheism, and vitalism with theism.

Meanwhile, however, certain things had happened which now made materialism seem less unscientific than when it was regarded solely in the light of the spontaneous generation issue. Toward the beginning of the nineteenth century chemistry had begun to flourish. At first this science seemed to offer support to the vitalistic position, in the sense that the abyss which it claimed separates the living from the non-living seemed to be confirmed also by chemistry. The chemist was able to synthetize as well as analyze inorganic substances, but with respect to organic substances, which exist in living beings, only analysis seemed possible. Their synthesis appeared to be possible only within the living beings themselves under the influence of their *vis vitalis*. When, however, in 1828 Wöhler had succeeded in synthetizing urea, it became evident that in principle all organic substances, even the most complex, could be synthetized in the test tube. Of course, this evidence did not prove that vitalism was wrong since the synthetic production of organic substances was not the same as the synthesis of *living* organisms. Nevertheless, it pointed in a direction which would gradually undermine faith in vitalism.

Vitalism was convinced that the living is essentially different from the non-living and thought that its conviction could be proved by physical science. This expectation, however, failed whenever it seized any concrete phenomenon to support its conviction. The same fate that had befallen the distinction between inorganic and organic compounds was destined to strike vitalism again and again. As soon as organic compounds had been synthetized, vitalism pointed out that the synthesis made by a living organism did not occur in the same way as synthesis in the test tube. For instance, from the fact that sugar did not change through fermentation into alcohol when the micro-organisms were killed, Pasteur drew this vitalistic conclusion: the specific way of the fermentation process cannot be exclusively attributed to the activity of certain chemical substances but has to be ascribed also to factors proper to life. Life, he held, has its own ways of doing things. Later, however, it became evident that these processes occur under the influence of ferments which can also produce their catalytic action outside the organism. In other words, there is question only of ordinary chemical processes, which can occur both inside and outside organisms.

Meanwhile vitalism continued to hold, so it seemed, one final ace: all the successes of science in synthetizing organic compounds in the test tube were useless as arguments against vitalism since the chemist conducting the experiments, himself, functioned as a higher principle than mere matter.[4] In these experiments, the vitalists argued, organic compounds arise through synthesis, but not by the forces of matter alone, because these forces are guided in their action by the thinking and acting of man. In other words, their artificial synthesis confirmed rather than contradicted the claim that the synthesis of chemical compounds in the living organism takes place under the directing influence of a vital principle.

Although this argument was correct—though by no means decisive—with respect to the syntheses that used to be made in the laboratory, it too had to be dropped. About a decade ago it became evident that amino acids, the building blocks of protein, can be synthetized in such a way that in principle the process can occur in nature, even without being directed by man, with the help of materials that likewise can occur in lifeless nature. It stands to reason that these syntheses are extremely important with respect to the theory of evolution, and we will therefore return to them in connection with this theory. At present we merely want to note that vitalism has been forced to abandon its entire line of thought concerning the synthesis of organic compounds. This defeat, however, does not mean that vitalism has had to give up all its arguments drawn from physical science. For there was question only of synthetizing non-living material structures and, important as these structures are in living organisms, they themselves are not living. The synthesis of living organisms has not yet been accomplished. In

---

[4]Cf., e.g., H. J. Jordan, *De causale verklaring van het leven,* Amsterdam, 5th ed., 1947, Ch. III.

this matter there are, at most, some tentative ideas about how such a synthesis could perhaps take place.[5]

Vitalism did not appeal only to chemical arguments, of course, but also to strictly biological proofs. Hans Driesch is one of the best known proponents of this type of argument, and his experiments with sea-urchin eggs are especially famous. His main proof was based on the development of the embryo and the regulative and regenerative phenomena manifesting themselves in this development. The normal development of cell division is such that there occurs a constantly increasing differentiation. If, however, in the two-cellular stage the two cells are isolated, they do not develop into two "half" embryos but into two complete individuals. From this experiment Driesch concluded that the cells in question are pluripotent. What will result from them through further division is not determined by spatially preformed physical and chemical structures, but by a principle, called "entelechy," which directs the physical and chemical forces to a goal, viz., the development of complete individuals.

The phenomena of regeneration also are very impressive. If one removes the lens from the eye of a salamander larva, a new lens develops. Such a phenomenon seems to point to a principle that safeguards the individual's integrity. This idea is strengthened further by the fact that the new lens does not develop in the normal way, from the epidermis, but from the edge of the iris, which normally has no function in the formation of the lens. This kind of phenomena, of which there are numerous examples, confirmed Driesch in his conviction that there exists an entelechy which controls the physical and chemical forces of the organism.[6] Entelechy, however, does not

[5]For examples of such ideas see A. J. Oparin, *The Origin of Life on Earth,* London, 1957; G. Allen, "Reflexive Katalysis, a Possible Mechanism of Molecular Duplication in Prebiological Evolution," *The American Naturalist,* vol. 91 (1957), pp. 65-78; S. L. Miller and H. C. Urey, "Organic Compound Synthesis on the Primitive Earth," *Science,* vol. 130 (1959), pp. 245-251; R. F. Nigrelli (ed.), "Modern Ideas on Spontaneous Generation," *Annals of the New York Academy of Science,* vol. 69 (1957), pp. 255-376.

[6]"A material system in space does not behave in the same way when it is left to itself as when it is controlled by an entelechy. In other words, the spatially localized factors represent only a part of the sum total of all factors on which organic events depend." Driesch, *Philosophie des Organischen,* Leipzig, 1909, vol. II, p. 349. "Ein materielles System im Raum verhält sich anders, wenn es sich selbst überlassen ist, als wenn es von Entelechie kontrolliert wird. Mit anderen Worten: Die im Raum lokalisierten Faktoren bilden nur ein Teil von der Summe aller Faktoren, von denen organisches Geschehen abhängt."

modify the action of chemical substances, but is able to suspend that action. It itself is not a chemical substance or a combination of chemical substances.[7]

No matter how impressive Driesch's arguments were, he did not succeed in permanently convincing the biologists. Strictly speaking, this lack of success is not surprising, for the way Driesch postulated his entelechy blocked the progress of biological research. If the physical and chemical forces in question were fully known and yet it was still not possible to explain the regulative and regenerative phenomena, then it would be meaningful to appeal to an entelechy. As the situation was, however, Driesch's postulate was an unjustified guess that frustrated rather than fostered biological research. Expressed in the terminology of the first chapter, entelechy was too much answer and too little question. And since for biology as a science the question was more important than the answer, it refused to worry about entelechy and quietly continued its investigation of the relevant phenomena. Its research soon showed that these phenomena were not at all as unqualifiedly purposive as they had first seemed.

For instance, with respect to the above-mentioned experiment with salamander larva, the new lens develops not only when the original lens is removed but also when it is simply pushed out of its place. Fortuitous stimuli also appear able to give rise to a new lens. Briefly expressed, the entire process seems to run its course in a rather deterministic-mechanical fashion. In its interplay with the experimenter, entelechy presents itself not at all as a free agent but rather as a blind reaction. All this does not mean, of course, that purposive process of normal embryonic development and the ability to correct disturbances of this process do not constitute a fundamental biological problem which cannot be solved by simply referring to causality. As E. Mayr correctly remarks, "No discussion of causality is complete which does not come to grips with the problem of teleology."[8] One should keep in mind, however, that to acknowledge the final tendencies that are unmistakably present in biological processes is not at all the same as ascribing them to an agent which is independent of causal factors and transcends them.

As the topic of causality and finality will be discussed later, here we merely want to remark that the path chosen by Driesch was destined to lead nowhere. Biology decided to take a different ap-

---

[7]Driesch, *op. cit.,* pp. 253 ff.
[8]"Cause and Effect in Biology," *Science,* vol. 134 (1961), pp. 1501-1506.

proach, it sought physically and chemically determinable factors which could be responsible for programming organic development. Recent discoveries seem to indicate that the structure of nucleic acids is responsible for this programming.[9]

Accordingly, even in its choice of biological arguments, vitalism was not especially fortunate. With respect to nearly all concrete points which it adduced to prove that the phenomena of life cannot be explained in a physico-chemical fasion, vitalism has been vanquished either because explanations have already been given or because they have proved to be possible in principle. As von Bertalanffy rightly remarks, "The history of biology is constituted by the refutation of vitalism."[10]

Although von Bertalanffy's remark is true, it does not mean that the last word has been spoken in the controversy between vitalism and mechanism. In making this assertion, we are not primarily thinking of the fact that the abyss between the living and the non-living has not yet been bridged, although the existence of this abyss remains a fact. All scientific explanations of vital phenomena continue to be based upon the pre-existing order of living structures. While the development of the ovum may be based on a programming, the ovum owes this programming to the genes of its parents. The origin itself of living structures continues to be a realm of daring speculations, of which as yet we do not have a clear idea.[11]

Nevertheless, something has been achieved since evolutionists in the second half of the nineteenth century almost made a dogma of abiogenesis. At present most biologists do not reject in principle the possibility of abiogenesis with respect to the origin of life, in spite of the fact that in the world open to direct experience life always originates from something living. The biologists' reason for this standpoint does not lie in any materialist dogmatism but in their confidence in the progressive character of physical science. The history of biology has sufficiently taught them that explanations which cannot be given today are likely to be possible tomorrow. Does this mean, therefore, that the capture of this last line of defense behind which vitalism can still entrench itself, the question of the origin of life, will imply that mechanism has been right and vitalism wrong in every respect?

---

[9]C. P. Raven, "The Formalization of Finality," *Folia biotheoretica,* no. V, Leiden, 1960.

[10]*Op. cit.,* p. 21.

[11]Cf. the references given in footnote 5.

A reply to this question demands many distinctions. As we have already mentioned, it is certainly not true that mechanism in its literal sense has been proved. Mechanical models have only a limited value in physics and, therefore, also in biology. Moreover, one cannot agree with classical mechanism that the phenomena of life can be fully understood in terms of the properties of elementary particles. To know the true properties of matter it is not sufficient to study them only in non-living structures, thereby regarding biology merely as applied elementary physics and chemistry. To discover the real possibilities of matter, one also has to study its living structures. Such a study may reveal new aspects of the general properties of matter, aspects which do not disclose themselves in a study that is restricted to inorganic structures.[12]

This assertion does not imply an affirmation of the vitalistic claim that different physical and chemical laws hold for living organisms, but it is fully in line with the direction taken by the development of physics itself and its critique of mechanistic thought. For physics has given up the idea that knowledge of elementary "atoms" is adequate and that the study of the structures formed by these "atoms" cannot essentially increase our knowledge.[13]

The objection could be raised that all this is essentially only a matter of details and leaves the main issue untouched. The main issue is that there seems in principle no essential difference between living and non-living since the phenomena of life also can be explained in a physico-chemical way. For, biology is becoming increasingly convinced that a living organism is nothing but a particular complex material structure without any mysterious factor making it a living being. True, abiogenesis has not yet been explained; but this failure must be attributed to our relative ignorance of the complex living structure itself, as well as of the potencies of non-living matter, rather than to a difference between living and non-living which would be beyond the grasp of physical science.

The phenomenon of anabiosis may be referred to in support of this claim. Certain organisms show themselves able to "survive" extreme situations, such as total dehydration or cooling to almost absolute zero. Biologically speaking, one has to assume that in such

---

[12]von Bertalanffy speaks in this connection about the necessity of enlarging physics and chemistry in order to deal with the problems of biology. *Op. cit.*, pp. 119 ff.

[13]Cf. Chapter III, Section 3. For a critique of atomistic thought in biology see C. H. Waddington, *The Nature of Life*, London, 1961, pp. 19 ff.

extreme conditions all processes of life have stopped. Since, however, the material structures of these organisms remain intact, or at least are not irreversibly modified, these organisms can subsequently begin to live again.

In the main, therefore, the history of biology seems to lead to the conclusion that mechanism was entirely right, or at least will eventually be entirely right. Yet even with respect to this main point, distinctions have to be made if we want to see to what extent this conclusion is correct.

The first question to arise in this connection is concerned with the competence of physical science. In the traditional dispute between vitalism and mechanism this question occupies a peculiar position. Both mechanism and vitalism started with the tacit presupposition that physics and chemistry were sciences which could give an all-encompassing and complete explanation of non-living material reality. Then they disagreed whether these sciences could also offer a complete explanation of living reality; mechanism gave an affirmative reply while vitalism answered in the negative. To prove that it was right vitalism looked for phenomena which could not be explained by these sciences although they were within the reach of their methods of observation. Its search was bound to be a failure, of course; and this failure was just as naturally bound to write the history of biology, for any unexplained phenomenon could only stimulate the biologist to search for its explanation.

The fundamental mistake of vitalism was it failure to recognize the true nature of physical science. This failure had two aspects. On the one hand, vitalism underestimated the power of physical science, and on the other, overestimated it. Physical science is an abstract science, which approaches given reality in a special way, namely, by means of external cognitive contact. Because of this abstract character, physical science never fully explains non-living material reality, for it is not the only possible way to consider this reality. On the other hand, physical science is not at all limited to a study of non-living material being. It is not only abstract but also universal, in the sense that it extends to all reality to the extent that this reality, in any way whatsoever, can be perceived by the senses. Plants, animals and man are just as much within its reach as inorganic reality.

Accordingly, by virtue of its abstract character, the limits of physical science are internal rather than being external in the sense that certain realms would lie beyond its reach. While it may be true that these internal limits manifest themselves more in the study of man, animals and plants than in non-living beings, nevertheless, in principle these limits are always there.

For this reason it is not right to speak of a mystery of life that would be beyond explanation, as certain vitalistic biologists like to do. We do not mean that there is no mystery, but this mystery is ultimately the mystery of all reality, whether living or non-living, human or not-human. Differently expressed, as physical science makes us understand more about the specific phenomena of life, the mystery will at most be transferred from the mysterious character of the living to the mysterious nature of all material reality. The progressive explanation of the phenomena of life simply makes matter all the more mysterious.

All this, however, does not imply that there is no essential difference between the living and the non-living. This question has, strictly speaking, not yet been raised. For, if physical science is an abstract science, then all reality which it investigates appears to it in one and the same perspective, viz., that of physico-chemical structures. From the standpoint of physical science the difference between living and non-living reality cannot be anything else but a difference in complexity of structure. Considered in itself, therefore, the fact that, according to biology, the phenomena of life and its origin can be explained in a physico-chemical way does not yet say anything about a difference in the level of being between living and non-living. Even if there is such a difference, it would not appear in any other way within the context of physical science than as a difference in physico-chemical structure.

We will revert to this question later. At present we merely wanted to show how complex the controversy between mechanism and vitalism really is. The whole dispute is permeated with many different kinds of problems, or rather with different levels of problems. Without an analysis of these different levels it is not possible to arrive at a clear judgment of what exactly the history of biology teaches us about the dispute between vitalism and mechanism. Let us see therefore what these levels of problems are.

3. The Different Levels of Problems

The preceding considerations contain several indications pointing to the necessary distinctions. As has become sufficiently evident from the development of biology, the dispute between vitalism and mechanism was primarily concerned with all kinds of problems that strictly belonged to physical science. In addition, however, there were also problems pertaining to the level of the theory of science, that of the philosophy of nature and that of metaphysics and religion.

The Level of Physical Science. The question whether organic compounds can be synthetized is a problem of physical science, a problem that could be, and has been, solved only by physical science. The same applies to the question whether the embryo is programmed in a physico-chemical way for development into an adult, and if so in what way. Even the question whether abiogenesis is possible is a problem that can at least be approached in the way proper to physical science.

The Level of the Theory of Science. Questions about the theory of science must be distinguished from those pertaining to the philosophy of nature. As we have mentioned above, the materialism of many biologists and evolutionists was based more on the belief that a physico-chemical explanation is possible than on the conviction that there exists nothing but matter. At any rate, in the struggle between mechanism and vitalism a difference in view regarding the competence of physical science played a role, and such a difference pertains to the realm of the theory of science. The strength of mechanism and materialism lay in the fact that they realized the universal character of the methods proper to physical science; their weakness, in disregarding its abstractness. In the course of the development of biology, both the abstractness and the universality of physical science revealed themselves clearly.

The universality of this science manifested itself when physical science's proper method of explanation was extended to the realm of vital phenomena and made it evident that the development of biology as a physical science proceeded along the line which had become discernible in the seventeenth century. At that time celestial and terrestrial matter were recognized as being identical; and, in its development, the successes achieved by biology proved convincingly that the matter of living beings was no other than that "unitary" matter of celestial and terrestrial bodies.

The abstract character of physical science likewise became more evident. By virtue of its method, physical science has only an indirect grip on the interiority that announces itself in living beings.

Studying reality in the perspective of physical science, the biologist sees appearing before him the various "layers" of nature—the non-living, the vegetatively living, the sensitively living and the human—as increasingly more complex structures. The vegetatively living being possesses all the complexity of inorganic reality and, in addition, the very special complexity of the living organism, which, according to biological conviction, must be regarded as a special form and a natural continuation of the inorganic. The same applies to the even more complex structures of animal and man. All that, however, is merely one aspect of the problem. For, to the increasing complexity of the externally observable structures, there corresponds, beginning on a certain level, a growing interiority culminating in man's self-consciousness.

Precisely this occurrence of interiority indicates that one cannot simply regard the distinction between the different levels of being as nothing but a difference in physico-chemical complexity. No matter how correct mechanism was in realizing the universal character of physical science, it certainly was wrong in overlooking its abstractness. Vitalism likewise failed to recognize the abstract nature of physical science for what it was. For, as we have seen above, by looking for arguments within the perspective of physical science, vitalism tacitly assumed that this science was able to arrive at complete knowledge of *inorganic* reality. The insufficiency of the approach proper to physical science with respect to the phenomena of life, vitalism had argued, was bound to disclose that life was something special.

Accordingly, neither mechanism nor vitalism had a clear idea of what physical science can or cannot do. In this respect the history of biology has shown that neither one nor the other was right.

The Level of Philosophy of Nature. From the preceding considerations regarding the competence of physical science, it follows that there is a third level of problems. This level is called the level of the philosophy of nature. The central question on this level is whether life must be regarded as a higher form of being than the non-living. The fact that the phenomena of life can be explained in the perspective of physical science does not at all dispose of this philosophical problem. Actually, this fact would render the philosophical question superfluous only if physical science were not an abstract science, only if this science were able to give us complete knowledge of reality. Unlike its function on the first level of problems, physical science itself cannot provide us with a solution to this question. This statement, however, does not mean that physical science cannot make an important contribution to its solution. We will consider this point more in detail in the following section.

The Metaphysico-Religious Level. Finally, there is still another level of problems that should be distinguished here. This level, of a metaphysical and religious nature, has become important in the dispute between vitalism and mechanism especially since the question of evolution had arisen. Several reasons in connection with the rise of the theory of evolution have contributed to making the metaphysico-religious aspect of the problem acute. First of all, the theory of evolution seemed to contradict the traditional view of creation; it explained the origin of nature differently from the book of *Genesis.* This divergence alarmed many Christians. They saw the theory of evolution as an attack on Christian faith, and made every effort to combat this new danger. Realizing that an unbridgeable abyss between living and non-living reality would make evolution an illusory theory, many Christians were inclined to support vitalism.

Moreover, as we have mentioned, both mechanists and vitalists generally assumed that inorganic reality could be completely explained by physical science. For this reason it seemed that the dispute over the possibility of fully explaining life by means of matter would also decide the question whether God's creative power was needed for the existence of life. The thesis that life cannot be fully explained in terms of non-living matter was simply equated with the claim that if life cannot be explained in a physico-chemical fashion, then it can be used as a proof from physical science for the necessity of a Creator, at least with respect to the living part of reality. The materialists, on the other hand, claimed that a mechanistic explanation of life would render the idea of creation superfluous. Matter alone was considered all-explanatory.

No matter what one thinks about the idea of creation, little philosophical reflection is needed to show that this new aspect of the struggle between mechanism and vitalism differed essentially from the question whether or not there existed a possibility of explaining vital phenomena in a physico-chemical way and also from the philosophical question whether or not an organism should be fully equated with an inorganic structure. The idea of creation is concerned with the mystery of why there exists any reality at all, regardless of whatever relations there are in this reality. In this matter it is very illuminating to read a passage of G. G. Simpson. He considers himself a materialist because he believes it is possible for physical science to explain all vital phenomena, inclusive of life's origin. Speaking about the special position of the question of creation, he says:

> This is not to say that the whole mystery has been plumbed to its core or even that it ever will be. The ultimate mystery is beyond the reach of scientific investigation, and probably of the human mind. There is neither need nor excuse for postulation of nonmaterial intervention in the origin of life, the rise of man, or any other part of the long history of the material cosmos. Yet the origin of that cosmos and the causal principles of its history remain unexplained and inaccessible to science. Here is hidden the First Cause sought by theology and philosophy. The First Cause is not known and I suspect that it never will be known to living man. We may, if we are so inclined, worship it in our own ways, but we certainly do not comprehend it.[14]

At this stage of our considerations, it is not important whether or not one agrees with Simpson's somewhat agnostic evaluation of the possibilities open to philosophy and theology. What matters here is that Simpson clearly sees that the problematics of creation are concerned with something which differs from the possibilities open to explanation through physical science. For this reason there can be mechanists who believe in God just as there can be vitalists who deny His existence.

The characteristic emotional tension which so often occurs in the controversy between vitalism and mechanism finds its explanation, to a large extent, in the fact that the various levels of problems and their connected fundamental positions are interwoven in the dispute. It is important, then, that these levels be first clearly distinguished. The demand for this distinction does not imply, of course, that these levels are entirely independent, for the clarification of problems raised on one level can make an important contribution to those arising on others. As could be expected, a fundamental role in these matters is played by the development of physical science, not so much, however, with respect to its concrete data as with regard to what we have called, in Chapter Two, the

---

[14]*The Meaning of Evolution*, New York, 1951, p. 134.

explicitation of that which is implicitly presupposed by physical science.

A clear example of this point is offered by the presupposition, later clarified by the history of biology, that everything material has fundamentally the same nature. It is especially this presupposition which is expressed in the "belief" that physical science can explain the phenomena of life and in the "belief" in abiogenesis, though the latter is still far from demonstrated. Mechanism, which lived in this "belief," owed its success to it, even though it is true that at first mechanism was much too narrowly interpreted, a narrowness which manifested itself in its conception of matter in general (cf. Chapter Three). If, then, the history of biology has shown that vitalism was wrong, this statement refers primarily and directly only to the first level of problems and not to the others.

Indirectly, however, precisely because it was the principal defender of the presupposition that all matter is fundamentally the same, mechanism has exercised its influence upon all the different levels of problems. First of all, of course, on the second level, where the competency of physical science was explicitly questioned. On this level the history of biology has, we think, made it abundantly clearly that physical science is universal, be it abstract, science. Precisely this universal aspect expresses in its own way the presupposition of the fundamental unity of everything material. With respect to the third level of problems, the state of being proper to the living, we had to note that the success of mechanism cannot at all decide this issue. Nevertheless, we must add that even this question cannot be considered independently of the unity of matter. An analogous consideration applies to the fourth level, that of creation. The unity of everything material forces the metaphysician and the theologian to purify the problem of creation from extraneous matters. An appeal to creation for the explanation of life may certainly not be substituted for a possible explanation by physical science. This question, however, will be discussed in Chapter Seven.

4. The Characterization of Life and Interiority

The topic which concerns us most in this chapter is the state of being proper to life. In the preceding pages only one point has become clear: if physical science will eventually succeed in explaining the phenomena of life and even its origin from non-living matter, this success does not determine the state of being proper to life;

although it is true, of course, that the unity of everything material, which is expressed in the possibility of such an explanation, makes an important contribution to the state of the question. The fact that the question remains undecided is connected with the manifestation in living reality of a new dimension, the dimension of interiority. As we have seen, many biologists regard this dimension so essential to life that they include it in the definition of life.

The objections against this inclusion have also been noted. One of them was that, on methodological grounds, physical science cannot speak of interiority. This objection is correct but not decisive, for the simple reason that physical science is an abstract science. In this way the objection is reduced to another question: Is biology fully characterized by being described as a physical science? Is there not spontaneously present in it another aspect, by virtue of which biology implicitly "knows" that it is interested only in material reality that is living?

If the situation were such that life could be unqualifiedly equated with interiority, there would be no problem. But the difficulty is that interiority is not everywhere present in life, which is precisely the reason why many object to its inclusion in the definition of life. True, Portmann tries to see an indication of this interiority in the typical but specifically different replies which all species of plant life give to the same material conditions.[15] But this is precisely the point where the difficulties arise; for exactly the same can be said about certain technical products. By virtue of their different construction, machines also react in different ways to the same external material conditions. Supplied with the same fuel and placed on the same runway, an airplane will fly but a motorcar will ride. Why, then, in the case of plants, should the different ways of reacting be attributed to anything other than their material structure?

Accordingly, to speak of interiority on the level of plant life seems to tend unduly in the direction of vitalism. Vitalism, of course, has no difficulty whatsoever with interiority because it accepts an entelechy over and above the material structure. For Hans Driesch interiority was able to manifest itself even on the vegetative level in the regulative function exercised by the entelechy. Such an entelechy, however, has never been found. There exists a regulative function,

---

[15]Portmann, *Probleme des Lebens,* p. 14. Cf. also Th. von Uexküll, *Der Mensch und die Natur,* Bern, 1953, Chapters V and VII.

but this function is enclosed in the dynamism of the material structure itself.

Nevertheless, one cannot simply reject the inclusion of interiority in the definition of life as a lingering symptom of vitalism. Two data are against such a rejection. Although they come from different spheres, their internal connection imposes itself irresistibly.

The first of these data is the unity of all life, as it reveals itself to the gaze of physical science. One finds the same fundamental cell structure everywhere, from the simplest unicellular being to the most complex organism, and, likewise, everywhere the same chemical composition. From the standpoint of physical science, life is one giant unity: "all life is the same." Within the perspective of physical science, the differentiation manifesting itself in life appears to be an increasing complexity of that which is essentially the same.

The second datum is that in the increasing complexity of physically observable structures, starting from a certain level, there is revealed a growing interiority, which culminates in man's self-consciousness. This growing interiority induces the biologist more or less spontaneously to consider the more complex structures as higher, not because of their difference in material complexity, but because of the interiority which these structures appear to make possible. By describing the structures as higher or lower, which from the standpoint of physical science is meaningless,[16] the biologist has recourse to his own self-experience, whether or not he is explicitly aware of this.

Let us add that, although this self-experience does not belong to the object of physical science, it is not entirely outside the realm of this science. Precisely as a scientist, the biologist "knows" about man's knowing, whether intellectual or sensitive. The biologist who finds some sense organs in animals knows what those organs mean. From his own experience he knows what an eye is and what it means to see. And even though it may be difficult for him to understand experience and knowledge as they are on the level of animal being, he knows that animals have a kind of interiority.

Not every form of life exhibits the interiority that characterizes the higher forms of life. Moreover, on methodological grounds biology is inclined to treat the phenomena of interiority as much as possible by way of registration. Despite this, however, the biologist who does not want to deny his own science cannot escape regarding

---

[16]For a discussion of this point see, e.g., Simpson, *The Meaning of Evolution,* Chapter VII.

interiority as most intimately connected with life. For the unity of life recorded by physical science places him before the following dilemma. If, on any grounds whatsoever, he refuses to take into account the first beginnings of interiority in the animal world, then he must either leave man entirely out of consideration or, on reaching man, make a leap which, strictly speaking, would place man entirely outside the animal world. But both alternatives militate against the unity of life, for this unity includes man.

Methodologically speaking, the biologist who does not want to speak of interiority may be able to justify his standpoint so long as there is question of a particular scientific approach; but as soon as the question of the essence of life arises, interiority can no longer be left out of consideration. For this reason there is something in favor of placing interiority from the very beginning within the biologist's field of vision. True, by doing this, the biologist sacrifices his methodical purity; but, on the other hand, he experiences this sacrifice as something that brings him closer to living reality in its integral totality than if he were to retain his methodical purity.[17]

No matter, however, what attitude biology assumes, if it wants to hold fast to the unity of life, there is no escape from regarding interiority as something characteristic of all life, even though this interiority manifests itself differently on different levels. For this reason, one is also justified in seeing a close connection between the relative autonomy or selfhood that characterizes the living individual and the interiority manifesting itself in it. In this way the objections against placing interiority in the definition of life are largely overcome.

The preceding considerations will grow stronger as soon as the theory of evolution is more systematically brought to bear upon the matter, for hitherto we have only given it fragmentary glimpses. If the unity of living beings, man included, is based not only on a structural relationship but also on a real genesis, a biological origin, then the interiority proper to higher forms of life cannot be an extrinsic addition to elements which these forms have in common with lower levels of life; but it will have to be an unfolding of something already present in an incipient way on these lower levels. In this respect, therefore, the theory of evolution makes our problem easier.

---

[17]These two possible biological attitudes are clearly mirrored in the twofold conception of such disciplines as animal psychology and animal sociology.

In a different respect, however, the evolutionary theory complicates the problem much more. The contemporary theory of evolution not only assumes that man has originated from lower organisms but also maintains the origin of life from non-living matter. As a consequence of this extension, the beginnings of interiority are supposed to be present not only in the lower forms of life but also in the inorganic world. Teilhard de Chardin boldly admits this consequence and holds that everything material, whether living or not, has a "within" and a "without."[18] Regardless of what one may think about the truth of Teilhard's idea, it certainly poses a challenge to one seeking to distinguish the proper character of life. Before attempting this task, let us first devote a brief explicit study to the theory of evolution.

---

[18]*The Phenomenon of Man,* Bk. I, Ch. III (pp. 67 ff. in Torchbook ed.).

CHAPTER FIVE

THE THEORY OF EVOLUTION

1. The "Belief" in Evolution

An introduction to the actual state of affairs in the theory of evolution can easily become a kind of anticlimax, especially if one's first acquaintance with the theory has been made through the works of biologists and paleontologists like Teilhard de Chardin, Huxley or Simpson. We do not mean, of course, that biology fails to offer any arguments, far from it. First of all, practically all biological disciplines, such as comparative anatomy, systematics, the study of the geographic distribution of species, embryology, physiology and ethology, point to a relationship between the species. This relationship alone, however, does not yet imply that all species should be regarded as related by way of a common origin. Secondly, and this is the reason why the relationship is considered to point to such an origin, paleontology has found many fossils which indicate that at least the higher forms of vertebrates originated *after* the lower forms. This sequence is taken to suggest that they have also originated *from* these lower forms.

Strictly speaking, however, nothing appears really demonstrated. In itself, this is nothing to be disturbed about with respect to a theory of physical science. One would almost feel inclined to add that the lack of proof is a blessing. For, the theory of evolution is very fruitful for biological thought precisely because it contains more questions than answers. It invites the biologist to pursue purposive research in all kinds of disciplines because it is able to interconnect many different matters.

Strange as it may seem, the theory of evolution has gained enormous credit also outside biology. This credit manifests itself not only in the far-reaching extrapolating conclusions drawn by prominent biologists and paleontologists, such as Teilhard, Simpson and Huxley, but also in the evolutionary ways of thinking adopted by non-biological circles. It would certainly be wrong to attribute this generalized evolutionary way of thinking solely to the theory of evolution, for, as we have noted in Chapter One, previous general thinking in terms of evolution has also influenced the biological "belief" in the theory of evolution. (The fact that the idea of evolution enjoys so much status finds its partial explanation in the idea of development and progress which had fascinated man long before the origin of the theory of evolution.) For this reason it is not extravagant to say that part of the credit which the theory of evolution enjoys in biology is derived from the general intellectual climate which, since the rise of a progressive physical science in the seventeenth century, was favorable for evolutionary thought.

The influence of this general climate would also be able to explain the peculiar position of the theory of evolution within biology. This position can best be described by calling it an "unshakeable belief" in evolution. In biology the theory of evolution is more than an hypothesis which still has to be verified. If it is still regarded as an hypothesis, then at least this hypothesis is viewed as unescapable—which is rather peculiar for an hypothesis. In the terminology we have adopted in Chapter Two, we would be more inclined to speak about it as a presupposition; but this term could be opposed on the ground that evolution appears in biology, very clearly as a result of scientific research and not as its condition. The peculiar status of the theory of evolution also manifests itself in another dispute which from time to time flares up in biological circles and which we will examine here briefly.

As is well-known, there are biologists who like to emphasize that evolution is simply a fact, while others claim that it is an hypothesis, formulated for the explanation of certain facts. This difference in terminology is not purely accidental but is connected with another peculiar aspect of the theory of evolution as a biological doctrine. From an epistemological standpoint, the theory of evolution is an interesting phenomenon. (On the one hand, it is a physical theory, intended to explain certain data of physical science; but on the other, it is also a kind of historical theory. As a physical theory, it makes certain statements regarding the mutability of biological species and tries to find its causes, such as mutation, reshuffling of hereditary factors and natural selection.) In this respect it is a general theory concerned with repeatable processes. In principle this theory is valid just as much for life on other planets as for life on earth, just as chemistry and physics are considered to be valid for the entire cosmos. As a historical theory, however, the theory of evolution attempts to reconstruct how *de facto* life has developed on earth. To solve this problem historical "documents" are needed, in the form of fossils and geological formations.

These two aspects of the theory are, of course, not unrelated, as we have already pointed out when we spoke about the arguments in favor of evolution. Paleontological and geological data invite the biologist to regard systematic relationships as relationships of descent. The same data supply arguments in favor of abiogenesis. There was a time when no life could exist on earth, and this datum gives rise to the physical problem of how abiogenesis is possible. However, even if abiogenesis could be experimentally brought about, this would not yet show how abiogenesis did *de facto* occur on earth. This historical problem would continue to exist. Similar considerations also apply to the evolution of species within the realm of life. Let us assume that an experimenter would succeed in producing an evolution that would go across the boundary of a species. His success would mean a giant step forward in the investigation of the causes of evolution, and much light would have been thrown upon the possible ways which evolution can take. Nevertheless, the path taken by it *de facto* on earth could still be determined only in combination with the "documents" of paleontology.

In the light of these two aspects of the theory of evolution one can also understand the dispute whether evolution should be conceived as a fact or as an hypothesis. From the standpoint of physical science the only "facts" are repeatable facts, phenomena that can be provoked or at least observed again and again at will, such as mutations or exchange of genes in genetics, homologies or analogies in comparative anatomy, similarities in embryonic development, or equality of chemical structure in biochemistry. Evolution itself, in its totality as a historical event, is not a process which the biologist can evoke at will; hence it cannot be a *fact* for him, but only an hypothesis, a theory intended to explain the facts. Only if he were able to bring about evolution at will, would he be willing to accept it unqualifiedly as a fact.

Those, however, who think in a more "historical" fashion are guided by different considerations and, consequently, use a different terminology. They think above all about what *de facto* has happened in the past, as testified by their "documents." If these documents are sufficiently trustworthy, then they have no other alternative but to call evolution a fact. This does not mean that the fact in question is perfectly certain, and even less that it is explained. But at any rate it is at least an assumed fact.

It should be evident that when evolution is spoken of as a fact in biological circles, this term cannot possibly mean a fact in the sense of physical science but refers to the historical sense of the word. All this, however, merely clarifies a terminological discussion in the light of the twofold character of the evolutionary theory. What remains unexplained is that the biologists so firmly "believe" in evolution, despite the fact that both the historical "documents" and the data of physical science are still insufficient.

As mentioned above, one could feel inclined to speak of this "belief" as a presupposition. Biologists often express their conviction by saying that evolution is the only possible hypothesis, at least within physical science. Now, if one asks what the basis is of this conviction, it becomes manifest that a certain evaluation of the method proper to physical science plays a decisive role, since in the eyes of the biologist there exists no other possibility of explanation except by means of evolution. For this reason Bernard Delfgaauw calls the theory of evolution an "ontological postulate."[1] This term is close to what we have called a "philosophical presupposition" and is therefore open to the same objection, viz., that the idea of evolution was introduced rather late in biology and even then only as the result of newly known facts.

Nevertheless, it is meaningful, we think, to consider the possibility that evolution is a presupposition of biology. This position can be held, of course, only if one is willing to take into consideration that the progress of a science may reveal and explicitate something which was implicitly contained in it as a presupposition. In other words, the idea of evolution owes its compelling character to the fact that it is, strictly speaking, only a further development of a certain fundamental principle. This fundamental principle is none other than the presupposition of the fundamental unity of everything material, which is the basis of physical science and permeates its entire method. On the basis of this same principle, the biologist "believes" in the possibility of explaining the phenomena of life through physical science, a "belief" which, as we have seen in the preceding chapter, constituted also the strength of mechanism.

In this way one can see the biologist's "belief" in evolution as a consequence of the presupposition that everything material possesses a unitary character, a consequence which becomes visible in biology through its use of the method proper to physical science. Or, if one

---

[1]*Geschiedenis en vooruitgang,* vol. I, Baarn, 1961, pp. 213 ff.

wants to formulate the matter even more fundamentally, "belief" in evolution flows from the presupposition of unity in mutability. Biology, of course, is not interested in this unity merely as the abstract unity proper to all universal theories, i.e., to all theories which encompass the whole of material reality, but also in relation to the production of concrete beings. If, then, there is mutability, as is shown by fossils, then this mutability must be understood in terms of this production; in other words, it must be understood as a unity of descent. To abandon this idea would mean giving up the possibility of explaining this mutability through physical science.

But all this is not decisive with respect to the specific explanation of evolution. (It merely points out that the theory of evolution contains both aspects that are proper to biology. First, the idea of evolution is an explicitation of the presupposition that everything material is fundamentally the same; this makes it possible for biology to assume that an explanation in terms of physical science is possible. At the same time, however, the idea of evolution is an explicitation of another fundamental conviction, namely, that life is something special and that its special character finds expression in the transmission, through generation, of its own being.) In the light of these remarks, the special significance of Darwin in the history of biology becomes clear.

2. The Significance of Charles Darwin

Darwin's (1809-1882) significance did not lie in his claim that the species of living beings were not constant, for Linnaeus (1707-1778), the founder of systematic biological classification, had already doubted that constancy. Neither did it lie in proposing the idea of evolution, for Jean Lamarck (1744-1829) had done so before him. The special significance of Darwin was that his theory of evolution attempted to describe a scientific mechanism according to which evolution could have taken place. He connected the historical element of development with the scientific element by appealing solely to general phenomena and theories that could be verified by physical science. How valuable his attempt was will be readily seen if we briefly consider the state of the evolutionary problem at the beginning of the nineteenth century, before Darwin stirred minds.[2]

At that time G. L. Cuvier (1769-1832) had already laid the foundations for paleontology. He managed to decipher the language of

---

[2]Cf. L. Eiseley, *Darwin's Century,* New York, 1958.

fossils by describing a method of "reading" the whole animal from its fossil fragments. In the process he noted how much early species differed from the more recent. Unlike his contemporary, Lamarck, however, he did not draw an evolutionary conclusion from this difference, but assumed that in the history of the earth there had from time to time been catastrophes, which disturbed the existing geological formations and destroyed the existing forms of life. After each such catastrophe a new period began through a new creation. The theory of catastrophes, he felt, explained why different periods had different species.

In Darwin's time opposition to this theory of catastrophes arose among geologists. Developing certain ideas of James Hutton (1726-1797), Charles Lyell (1797-1875) countered Cuvier's theory with the thesis that whatever had happened geologically on earth should be fully explained by the physical and chemical forces that continued to operate on earth. This theory is known as "actualism." Here one can easily recognize the procedure of physical science, which analyzes every concrete phenomenon according to general and immutable laws, regardless of its occurrence in the past or in the present.

In their actualism Hutton and Lyell remained fully in line with the physical science of Galileo and Newton. These two physicists had abandoned the ancients' view that celestial bodies possessed a different nature than terrestrial bodies; they had replaced the two mechanics, one for celestial bodies and one for terrestrial bodies, by a single mechanics able to explain both fall motions on earth and the revolutions of stars and planets. In a similar way Hutton and Lyell refused to accept successive geologies applicable to successive geological periods. While there could be reasons to distinguish different geological periods, the laws applying to them were immutably the same. The existing physical and chemical science could explain the origin and end of former geological formations.

Strange as it may seem, these actualists felt no more inclined to evolutionism than were the adherents of the theory of catastrophes. Yet their reluctance can be understood. For the theory of evolution presents not only a *change* of species but also a kind of progression, with lines that ascend in time from simple to more complex organisms and, at the same time, with the gradual manifestation of phenomena of life which the biologist, appealing to his self-experience, spontaneously refers to as "higher." "Higher" and "lower," however, are qualifications entirely foreign to the spirit of physics. As we have seen in the preceding chapter, they point to the special place which biology occupies in the physical sciences. But one can hardly expect a geologist, who deals only with inorganic nature, to regard one "random" geological formation as more developed or "higher" than another. In this sense all mountains are equally "high" for him. Understandably, the acceptance of biological evolution appeared in the eyes of the actualistic geologists to be a tacit appeal to principles outside physical science which were supposed to orientate the process of evolution from low to high. Evolution seemed to include vitalism.

Darwin managed to solve the impasse by assuming that the development of the species must be subject to explanation by physical science. By extending the line of reasoning followed by actualism, Darwin intuitively opted for the mechanistic standpoint. In doing so, he showed bold confidence that the future would justify his choice—any kind of nineteenth century mechanism was practically forced to do so anyhow. It also stands to reason that the theory of evolution became involved in all the misunderstandings which characterized the controversy between mechanism and vitalism. As an additional contributing factor to those misunderstandings, Darwin's explanation of evolution, although perhaps right in principle, was still without a sufficient foundation.

As a matter of fact, even today a solid foundation is lacking. Yet no modern biologist doubts evolution, even though the way it happened is not at all clear yet. True, thanks to genetics, which was hardly known in Darwin's time, we know a little more than he about the way the evolution of species could have been brought about through factors he named or described, such as random variations, isolation and natural selection. What has, however, changed fundamentally since Darwin is man's confidence in the method of physical science in general. Due to its many successes, this method enjoys so much credit that now man is also willing to entrust to it the solving of the problem of evolution. Of course, even today the same objections made by the actualists still hold. Even today the whole of evolution remains a mystery. The theory of evolution in general is, as we have seen, essentially based on "belief" rather than anything else. Its more special theories, such as neo-Darwinism, retain a strongly speculative character and are based on extrapolations which go far beyond experimental possibilities. While genetics has made meaningful experimentation possible, these experiments remain, strictly speaking, marginal phenomena. They always presuppose the total organization of the organism, and on the basis of this organization the biologist proceeds with his experiments. The mutations studied or produced are tiny changes and hardly touch the total structural plan of the organism in question. None of the mutations studied in the *Drosophila* have ever changed a *Drosophila* into anything that was not a *Drosophila*. In viruses one can observe numerous changes of properties, but the viruses do not cease to be viruses.[3]

Genetic experiments always remain within narrow limits. Whether they can be said to transcend the boundaries of species depends more or less on the definition selected to describe the species. For this reason passing the boundaries of a species is less important as a criterion for the validity of evolution than is the general observation that the experimental results still remain exceedingly limited. They provide a measure of reasonable support, but no more than that, for Darwin's fundamental idea. The latter was cautious enough to restrict himself in his *The Origin of Species* (1859) to the development of *species*. On the one hand, it is certain that changes take place through mutations which promote the random variations and thus furnish a basis for natural selection. On the other, it remains provisionally a matter of speculation whether the sum total of these micro-changes can explain the full wealth of life.[4]

The great obstacles to the execution of Darwin's program are, we think, of a twofold nature. In the first place, our experiments lack the time scale which was at the disposal of natural evolution. Secondly, and this is even more serious, the problems faced in the theory of evolution are none other than the problems of biology itself. As long as biology has not succeeded in the program that is, so to speak, "normal" for it, viz., the explanation of the phenomena of life by means of physical science, how can it even hope to be successful with the problems of evolution? The inherent difficulty of the biological process was precisely the reason the actualists did not feel attracted to the theory of evolution. So long as it is not evident how a certain structure, observable by physical science, necessarily calls for the phenomena of sense life (to limit ourselves to this point), biology

---

[3]Cf. F. C. Bawden, "Evolution and Viruses," *Symposium on Evolution,* Pittsburgh, 1959.
[4]Cf. the critical introduction of W. R. Thompson to Darwin's *The Origin of Species* in the Everyman's Library ed. of this work, London, 1958.

will inevitably fall short in any attempted explanation of evolution, because there is no escape from the fact that these phenomena have occurred in evolution. The theory of evolution cannot simply disregard the fact that it deals with an ascent from the lower to the higher and not merely with a differentiation of existing species already having their organization.

(Therefore, as soon as Darwin had proposed his views, the question of abiogenesis was brought to bear on the theory of evolution. For no scientific explanation of the phenomena of life is possible unless the explanation also accounts for the structure of the organism itself. And this structure has to be understood in terms of physical science; hence it is also natural to assume that the living has originated from the non-living. Otherwise it would not be possible to have a consistent program of scientific research. "Belief" in the theory of evolution is nothing but belief in the possibility of explaining the phenomena of life by way of physical science. By incorporating abiogenesis into their program, the mechanists, evolutionists and materialists indicated that they were intuitively aware of this identity.)

3. Confusion of the Various Levels of Problems Involved in Evolution

This extension of the program pursued by the theory of evolution, though only a logical consequence of Darwin's initial plan, made it a rather ambitious undertaking. In the same way it was logical to extend the program to include the origin of man in the theory of evolution. This second extension caused even more resistance than the question of abiogenesis, especially because physical science simply did not have the means to execute and verify even a fraction of its ambitious program. Any serious scientific discussion was, strictly speaking, impossible. Proponents of evolution constantly had to have recourse to far-reaching and provisionally uncontrollable extrapolations. Hence it is easy to understand why the theory of evolution provided philosophers and theologians with gratefully accepted opportunities to take potshots at the evolutionists and why the latter returned the fire in the form of antiphilosophical and antitheological tracts. Since proper arguments were lacking, the temptation to have recourse to non-biological weapons was too great.

Undoubtedly, the theory of evolution touched all kinds of general problems. By asking a question about the origin, it made it almost impossible to avoid the problematics of creation in connection with the theory of evolution. Rather, this problematics was automatically involved in it. For, until then Christians had always read the story of the book of *Genesis,* not only as a message that all reality ultimately owes its origin to God, but also as a reply to all kinds of concrete questions about this reality itself. The question the theory of evolution asked about the origin of species and of life itself was not a new question. Though man had often asked that question before, he thought the Bible answered it. It was not yet realized at the time that the answer found in *Genesis* was in part clothed in terms of everyday experience.

In this way the theory of evolution came in conflict with the traditional picture of creation, for this picture was colored by the then current idea that species are constant. That the Bible thinks in terms of constant species is just as obvious to modern exegesis as it is unimportant, but the situation was different in the past. It is interesting to see how, for example, Linnaeus connected precisely the idea of constant species with that of creation. In 1738, when still fully convinced of the constancy of the species, he wrote: "There are as many species as there are forms produced by the Infinite Being *ab initio.*" In 1751 he said: "We count as many species as there are forms created *in principio.*" In 1764 it became: "Therefore, there are as many species as there exist today diverse forms or structures of plants."[5] The more Linnaeus began to doubt the constancy of species, the less he appealed to creation.

The theory of evolution, however, came into conflict not only with the accepted picture of creation but, in the eyes of many, it seemed to make the whole idea of creation superfluous. For, the species no longer needed to be explained through a supernatural cause, and whatever was able to be explained seemed to be withdrawn from the need for an appeal to creation. One can understand the reaction; however, it cannot be claimed that no one realized that the cause of creation was not just another cause in the series of all

---

[5]Cf. W. Zimmermann, *Evolution,* Freiburg i. Br., 2nd ed., 1954, p. 209. M. J. Sirks in his article "Rondom de 'Origin of Species'," *De Gids,* vol. 122 (1959), p. 24, makes the following comment on these successive definitions: "A correct translation is not easy to give. What is meant by *ab initio* in 1738? Does it mean 'in the beginning' or 'since the beginning'? And regarding the *in principio* of 1751, does it mean 'in the beginning' or 'in principle'? It does not seem to be excluded that in both definitions Linnaeus was already thinking about the origin of new species after creation. In his definition of 1764 the bond with creation became even less and the recognition stronger that after creation new species had come into existence."

causes. One has only to read the leading theologians of the past to become convinced that they realized the special position of the First Cause.

However, apart from the fact that their analyses were not generally known, there existed, as a matter of fact, such an ingrained habit of appealing to the Creator to explain all kinds of things that the causality of creation could hardly be regarded as anything but a cause among other causes. Neither the evolutionists nor the antievolutionists were responsible for the common confusion of entirely different levels of problems; this confusion was already present. Only the progressive development of physical science gradually made it possible to distinguish these levels with sufficient clarity. Only when physical science was able to give real explanations could it become evident what exactly the problems were which this science could claim as its own. Likewise, only then did it become possible to raise the epistemological issues in a clearer fashion and to recognize that the issues of philosophy and theology were *sui generis* problems.

In the nineteenth century this clarity had not yet been reached. Unsurprisingly, therefore, theologians and philosophers had recourse to biological arguments and biologists did not hesitate to wield philosophical and theological weapons. Neither party can be accused of muddle-headedness, for the confusion reigning in the nineteenth century resulted simply because the question about the competency of physical science with respect to the explanation of life could not yet be clearly raised. Physical science did not have a sufficient grasp of its own problems, and for this reason its possibilities and limitations did not yet manifest themselves clearly. And since physical science could not yet adequately play its role in the dialogue of minds, philosophy and theology likewise were unable to view their problems from a purely philosophical or theological standpoint. Their problems remained mixed up with all kinds of primitive conceptions in matters of physical science.

What was particularly confusing in the whole affair was that the self-styled materialists, who undoubtedly were most clearly aware of the possibilities open to physical science, realized the universal character of the scientific method but not its intrinsic abstractness and consequent limitation. This failure to see the limitation of physical science provoked, and rightly so, the opposition of all those who felt intuitively that physical science was limited; yet they did not have the same awareness of its universality. The latter were convinced that, no matter how many things physical science would be able to explain, it could not explain everything. With due changes, everything that has been said in the preceding chapter about the different levels of problems in the controversy between mechanism and vitalism applies also to the dispute around the theory of evolution.

Since Darwin brought the theory of evolution to the center of interest, much has undoubtedly been clarified in the controversy between mechanism and vitalism and, therefore, also indirectly in the dispute around the theory of evolution. Nevertheless, there still remain many unsolved problems. This statement does not refer, at least not directly, to purely biological problems but rather to questions concerned with matters of epistemology (the theory of science) and philosophy of nature which, because the biological issues are not yet clear, remain more or less unsolved. We do not mean to imply that these respective levels of problems are not distinct, but only that philosophical reflection has to remain uncertain as long as the preparatory work is not yet sufficiently completed by the progress of science and the possibilities that reveal themselves in that progress.

As a philosophical reflection which wants to explicitate the philosophically relevant matters revealed in the pursuit of physical science, philosophy cannot escape dependence upon the progress of this science. However, philosophy is not entirely dependent upon this progress, or even primarily dependent upon it. Awareness of this relative independence is just as important as awareness of the relative dependence. The history of the theory of evolution clearly demonstrates this point. Certainly, it is not true that it was impossible one hundred years ago to see that extending evolution to man did not reduce man to mere matter, as the materialists claimed. Then, as well as now, that doctrine was opposed by the primordial datum that *man* himself was the one who pursued science and formulated the theory of evolution. No matter how much the evolutionary theory made material reality in a certain respect the origin of all reality, in another respect it was precisely man himself who functioned as that origin. For it was man who asked about his own origin, it was man for whom matters became clearer.

An often raised question, especially among evolutionists, is whether it was not fundamentally incorrect to regard evolution as a process oriented to man and to consider forms of life as higher or lower according to their closeness to the human form of life. Was not such a view a form of anthropomorphism and, therefore, unacceptable to an objective science? How would an amoeba, a salamander or an eagle evaluate the various forms of life and the evolutionary processes? Such questions can receive only one meaningful reply, which at the same time is wholly effective, viz., that the theory of evolution is unavoidably an exclusively human affair. It would be wrong to consider this reply biologically irrelevant, for biology, as bio-*logy*, is precisely an affair of the human *logos*. Eliminating this *logos* from biology eliminates biology itself, no matter what the actual state of affairs in biology is.

The emphasis we placed in Chapter One on the importance of physical science for philosophy was not primarily concerned with what this science teaches us about man as object but, rather, with what it reveals about man as subject. Yet these two aspects are intimately connected. Like any other science, physical science can make assertions about man as object only because man as subject endeavors to find clarity about himself in science. Man himself is always involved in advance, he knows in advance about himself prior to any scientific research. The theory of evolution derives much of its interest precisely from the fact that it confronts man, in a most radical fashion, with this original subject-object tension, for it is concerned with the origin of man. In this theory man tries, as it were, the impossible by speaking about himself at a time when he did not yet exist. He speaks about the cosmos-without-man, about life on earth before man existed; yet he is present to that cosmos, for otherwise how would he be able to speak about it? An escape from this paradox seems to lie in representing the theory of evolution simply as a kind of subjective projection, a human projection of how *man conceives* reality-without-man, but that is too easy an escape. It disregards the claim which physical science and man himself make on truth. While the theory of evolution may be a human projection, it is a projection orientated to reality. In it man aims at his own prehuman past and, therefore, is of necessity at the same time both present to and absent from it.

One who is aware of this subject-object tension, existing in every science but especially in the theory of evolution, will understand how impossible it is to postpone the philosophical questions and answers until physical science has been able to supply its clarifications. Such a demand would be equal to the elimination of the subject as subject. Man would immerse himself in the evolution of science without wanting to be present to this evolution. It is possible, of course, for a man who has assumed a particular scientific attitude of mind to become, as it were, immersed in that attitude. In a certain sense, we must say that such an immersion is not only possible but even necessary. For the best possible service that physical science can render to philosophy is to pursue science with the maximum of openness of mind.

On the other hand, there is a big difference between assuming such an attitude consciously and deliberately, for the sake of man's tendency to self-knowledge, and simply becoming immersed in that attitude. If science is to play its true role as a human function, the man of science must be conscious of his cognitive attitude, thereby transcending it. Let us add that he cannot avoid doing this anyhow. This inevitability touches perhaps the most essential point. The true choice facing man is not between simply immersing himself in science, thereby eliminating himself as the subject, and deliberately pursuing science to arrive at greater self-knowledge of the subject. The choice which man really has to make is always a matter of opting either for uncritical philosophizing or for critical philosophizing, either for trying uncritically to account for the meaning of science or for attempting to do it in a critical way. No matter what the possibilities of man are, he cannot eliminate himself as a subject.

That the preceding considerations are not idle speculations of a philosopher is proved by the entire history of the theory of evolution. That the debate became so passionate shows how much man realized that he himself was involved in this theory. The fact that these discussions were rather uncritical should not be attributed solely to the state in which philosophy and science were at that time. Part of the explanation lies in the fact that certain authentic data, which were more or less convulsively obliterated, refused to stay buried. They made themselves felt in the discussions, but in an uncritical fashion. Even the materialist, who thought that there was nothing but matter or who saw nothing but the method of physical science, implicitly confessed, by the heat of his participation in the debate, that he too saw that man as a subject was at stake in it. He neglected, however, in his reflection upon man to pay explicit attention to the consequences of man's involvement as a subject. This lack of critical sense can be attributed not only to the materialists. Their opponents also suffered from it, although in their case this lack assumed the form of a blindness to the unique contribution physical science would be able to make. They refused to critically inspect the traditional forms in which the philosophical and religious values had been embodied in the past.

The lesson, then, to be drawn from history, cannot be that philosophical reflection must be postponed until the problems of physical science have been clarified. (On the contrary, this lesson is that man must dare to philosophize on the basis of authentic data that are already present, but always with the willingness to take up again the fundamental themes in the light of new data that becomes disclosed in the course of time.) Only in this way can each successive generation play the role that falls to it. Let us try now, in this spirit, to consider critically what the theory of evolution can contribute to man's view of himself and his world. How does he see himself in the *scala naturae,* the "scale of nature," to use an old metaphor endowed with new life by the theory of evolution?

CHAPTER SIX

THE SCALE OF NATURE

1. The Major Realms of Reality

In the chapter about life we concluded that biology, on the one hand, presupposes the unity of everything material, as is evidenced by the application of the scientific method to the phenomena of life, and on the other, maintains that life is something special. While it recognizes that the living organism is a particular material structure, biology knows that there is something special to this structure, as is evidenced by the presence of interiority. True, interiority does not manifest itself in all phenomena of life; but, nonetheless, it appears to be so intimately connected with the structure of living beings that many biologists are willing to accept interiority as a characteristic of life. As we have mentioned also, there is a tacit reference to the biologist's self-experience when he speaks about interiority in this connection.

The occurrence of interiority also gives rise to the philosophical problem concerning the distinction between living and non-living, the problem of the state of being proper to them. This problem will perhaps divide itself into two, viz., the demarcation of purely vegetative life from the non-living and the demarcation of vegetative life from sensitive life. While this question will have to be discussed later, we may already make the remark that since the discovery of micro-organisms, biology has drawn a less pronounced distinction between plant and animal than between life and non-living. Even if a biologist accepts abiogenesis, this acceptance does not mean that the boundary between living and non-living has been abolished in his eyes. Although life may once have arisen from the non-living, since then the boundary between the two has been closed to make room for the inexorable axiom: "Omne vivum ex vivo" (every living being originates from a living being).[1]

---

[1] This does not mean, of course, that the factors which in the past made abiogenesis possible are now no longer operative. However, as a matter of fact, non-living material reality no longer has a chance to evolve into life because organic compounds that would develop now would at once be used as food by already existing life. In this way any incipient abiogenetic evolution is cut short.

97

True, it is not easy to define the living explicitly in a way that separates it sharply from the non-living. There are, moreover, structures, such as viruses, which make us think on the one hand of living organisms and on the other of inorganic structures. All this, however, does not cause the biologist to doubt the fundamental distinction between living and non-living, no matter how he conceives their distinction. But the distinction between plant and animal is something that, biologically speaking, is much less important. The controversy between vitalism and mechanism concerning the distinction between living and non-living is not paralleled by a dispute about the exact nature of the distinction between plant and animal.[2]

Such a parallel, however, returns as soon as there is question of a distinction in the animal realm between mere animal and man. Here, in many respects, though not in all, the dispute between mechanism and vitalism occurs again on a new level. No vitalist, of course, ever doubted that the living being is *also* a material structure, but he questioned the assertion that a living being was nothing but a material structure. Likewise, no one ever seriously doubted that man is *also* an animal, but there was doubt about the exact difference which distinguishes man from other animals. Does this distinction arise from the presence in man of a principle that differs from the entire order of materiality, such as a spiritual soul; or is it merely a development of certain capacities that are also found in animals?

On the other hand, the parallel between the problematics of living and non-living and that of human and non-human should not be exaggerated. The feature distinguishing the living from the non-living always remained somewhat mysterious and, at any rate, was not directly attainable, while that of man could be immediately reached. In his self-consciousness man's spiritual soul was present to itself. Hence, there was no question here of concluding to the existence of a special principle from external phenomena, as had to be done with respect to the soul of a plant or animal. In his self-presence man was aware that he was a subject, a light to himself. Any attempt to eliminate man's being-a-subject by means of arguments seemed but another confirmation of man's subjectivity. For

---

[2]Generally speaking, only philosophers try to develop the distinction between plant and animal. For an example see Henri Bergson's classic, *Creative Evolution*, Ch. II.

declaring that man was a purely material structure, as the materialists did, was always a declaration coming from a self-evaluating
subject. Clearly the very existence of a spiritual soul could not be
denied, and the discussion could be concerned only with the way in
which spirit and matter in man were related. Was there either a
spirit which, being in principle independent of the body, was merely
present in it in a temporary way or a spirit which was essentially one
with the body?

Perhaps the problem should be radically restated, so that the entire
parallelism with the controversy between mechanism and vitalism
disappears. Do perhaps all differences in the material world disappear entirely in relationship to man as a subject? Should the whole
of material reality, as it appears to the subject, be perhaps regarded
only as a phenomenon of the subject, a phenomenon of consciousness?
For what else can we affirm as reality than that of which we are conscious? Does anything else exist for the subject apart from phenomena
in the subject's consciousness? To examine all such views in detail
would be impossible, for it would mean the writing of a history
of philosophy. Yet their mere enumeration sufficiently shows that,
no matter how evident man's self-consciousness is, this self-consciousness is not sufficiently differentiated to let man have a clear and
distinct idea of himself.

If, however, man, who is presence to himself, cannot arrive at
clarity about himself, it is not surprising that he also experiences
difficulties in determining the exact nature of the living as distinct
from the non-living. As we have said, a reference to man's self-
experience consciously or unconsciously plays a role in his characterization of life, whether he limits himself to the original description of life as self-movement or, like Portmann, presents a more
elaborate description. Thus it is not surprising that man's cognitive
grasp of life remains extremely deficient. And the same applies also
to his grasp of matter. Regardless of what one thinks about matter,
it is certain that man, somehow, is also matter, or at least appears as
matter. If, however, man were fully himself, then he would know from
within, through his self-presence, what matter is, either because he
would be matter-present-to-itself or because as spirit he would see
the exact character of his bond with matter or, finally, because he
would realize why he would have to conceive things as material.

No matter how one looks at it, the limitation of man's self-presence
seems to play a role in the whole range of problems we are con-

sidering. This role, however, is not purely negative, in the sense
that we should be resigned to remaining forever ignorant of its solution. The limitation in question is not a purely facticitous situation
without any inner tension; we experience that limitation as a challenge. Precisely because of this challenge, every period of history
has witnessed new philosophical efforts to arrive at clarity. For the
same reason science, in its own way, also contributes, to the philosophical clarification, as should be evident from the preceding
chapters.

For instance, in the first chapter we saw how important physical
science is for man's understanding of himself. In the third chapter
we noted that physics and chemistry contributed not only to giving
man such knowledge of matter that he could better calculate and
control the forces of matter, but if also contributed indirectly to a
clarification of the philosophical problems of matter. Chapter Four
explained how the history of biology has done much to purify the
controversy between mechanism and vitalism and indirectly, therefore, also to remove extraneous issues from the philosophical discussion concerning life. Finally, the fifth chapter showed that the
theory of evolution is not only biologically important but also steers
philosophical reflection along certain lines.

All this indicates that the interaction between scientific research
and philosophical self-reflection contains the possibility that man's
self-consciousness is characterized by growth. We will develop this
point in more detail later. At present we merely ask in what direction
the theory of evolution wants to steer us in our reflections upon the
three great realms of reality indicated by the terms matter, life and
spirit.

The first point to be made in this respect is that, hitherto, the
theory of evolution has not done much more than suggest that
somehow the realm of life first developed from non-living material
reality and then branched out in many directions. At the same
time, there is supposed a certain development from lower to higher
forms of life, culminating in man. The suggestion is made but the
explanation is still largely missing. However, the term "explanation" should be correctly understood here. The theory of evolution
is primarily interested in explaining matters in terms of physical
science; in other words, it wants to approach material reality by way
of external cognitive contact.

2. The Possibilities and Limits of Explaining Evolution Through Physical Science

To offer a satisfactory scientific explanation of evolution means to discover in the structures of inorganic reality a capacity and tendency that leads of necessity to the formation of more complex structures, which in their turn would be able, and under certain conditions would of necessity have, to form simple living structures. Regarding this point—the formation of living structures—there are many misunderstandings due especially to the great emphasis placed on the element of chance in the theory of evolution. Undoubtedly, this element of chance is a very real factor, but it should never close our eyes to the fact that the scientific explanation of evolution is never based on chance but on the capacity and tendency of the component elements to form more complex structures.

The synthesis of amino acids will illustrate this point. As we mentioned in Chapter Four, there are in principle two possibilities for such a synthesis. The first or normal way could be called the "guided" synthesis. The chemist selects a certain compound as his basis and exposes it to certain reagents. The resulting compound is then purified, isolated and again exposed to certain reagents, and so on, until the desired amino acid is obtained. Briefly, the entire synthesis is carefully thought out and guided by thought. Nothing is left to chance.[3] In the second form of synthesis, however, chance is deliberately brought into play. Here the synthesis is based on chemical compounds which, it can be reasonably supposed, can meet one another by chance in nature; and these compounds are exposed to the action of factors to which they could also be exposed by chance in nature.

Accordingly, chance plays a role, but certainly not the main role. The fact that CH_4, NH_3, H_2O and H_2 in given conditions form amino acids is based on the fact that the elements C, N, H and O have an affinity to enter into certain combinations, such as, in the present case, those of amino acids. The natural conditions may happen to be more favorable in one case than in another, but there is no variation at all in the capacity and tendency to form amino acids.

Speaking about the origin of life at a time when but little was known about biochemistry, Teilhard de Chardin[4] resorted to a special

---

[3]Chance, of course, continues to play a role even in this case. The chemist, however, selects the conditions in such a way that the molecules cannot avoid meeting, even though he has no control over them individually.

[4]*The Phenomenon of Man*, Bk. I, Ch. II, Sect. 3 (Torchbook ed., p. 65).

kind of energy, so-called "radial energy," to explain the formation of constantly more complex structures. The ordinary energy situation apparently did not seem sufficient to him. However, such an appeal to "radial energy" obviously more or less eliminates physical science. The whole idea has a vitalistic tinge.

Biochemistry limits itself to "ordinary" energy. Its task as a physical science is to explain on physical grounds why amino acids can give rise to protein and also why all the other compounds necessary for life can arise. Let us add that the term "can" is equivalent here to "must" if the conditions are favorable.

The same procedure is repeated on the level of life, but now with the help of biological considerations, for there is question of the viability of the various biological organisms. Chance "decides" here about the favorable or unfavorable conditions for the change of the organisms, but not about the intrinsic viabilities of the variations. As J. van der Vecht rightly remarks, "Variation, as the product of mutation and recombination, supplies the materials for selection. Variation, however, always has an existing starting point in the form of the total complex of genes belonging to the individuals which compose the population. For this reason the variation is always—and in the first instance on the molecular level—determined by the possible changes of that which is already present. Selection tests these given possibilities primarily for their viability."[5]

For understandable reasons the theory of evolution since Darwin has always greatly emphasized the element of chance in its explanation of the evolutionary process. Yet, really, this element is only concerned with a secondary aspect. The time has not yet come to give a more primary explanation, for such an explanation would require much more scientific knowledge of the vital processes than man can boast at present.

If not even the abiogenesis of simple organisms has been explained and the question of the possibility of abiogenesis has not yet been sufficiently answered, is there any wonder that so much is still lacking in the scientific explanations of evolution? In particular, the origin and first development of man remains a great mystery, even from the standpoint of physical science. It is good to draw attention to these deficiencies, not in order to undermine "belief" in evolution, but to illuminate the enormous program this "belief" implies. In speculating about the feasibility of executing this program, one can-

---

[5]*Rijkdom der verscheidenheid,* Groningen, 1963, p. 12.

not avoid a very heavy reliance on the "goodwill" which physical science has acquired and, at the same time, a penetration deep into the unexplored. Briefly put, to execute the program one has to project future developments of science, only small fragments of which are given now. The only justification one can offer for such a hazardous undertaking is that the theory of evolution, as a program, demands them and that the speculations of evolutionists have often anticipated developments in rather uncritical ways. Let us consider, then, what the program of the future would include.

Hitherto we have paid attention only to the scientific aspect of evolution and its problems of explanation. They are all concerned with discovering the natural affinities in matter to form biological structures. Exactly how these affinities have in the past formed these structures is of secondary importance here and belongs, strictly speaking, more to the historical aspect of evolution. More important, however, is that whatever wealth of potential physical science may discover in matter for forming all kinds of biological structures, this discovery will not be that of the potential interiority that culminates in man's self-consciousness. For precisely this aspect of life escapes discovery through the method of physical science, which always approaches reality by way of a cognitive contact through the external senses.

On the other hand, it is possible to observe a certain correspondence. As soon as a certain degree of complexity is reached in the biological structure, there also occur certain phenomena of interiority. Surveying the scale of nature with a scientific glance, we note that there is an increasing complexity which manifests itself, on the one hand, in a greater differentiation and, on the other, in a greater integration. To the growing complexity of externally observable structures there corresponds, starting from a certain level, a growing interiority, with which we are most familiar in man's self-experience. These correspondences can be carefully investigated. What is, for instance, the relationship between, on the one hand, seeing and the psychological structures implied in it, and on the other, the biological structures which make seeing possible? However, even if it would have been determined that only one biological structure makes seeing possible, this knowledge would not tell us what seeing really is. The nature of sight itself is known only from our own experience.

To establish that there are such correspondences is not easy, not even on the sensitive level, and becomes still more difficult when one turns to man's self-consciousness. On the other hand, no matter how difficult it is to establish the exact correspondence, the only possible road here evidently lies in establishing the correspondence. For in what other way than by correspondence could one discover that a certain biological structure is accompanied by self-consciousness? Hardly anyone will refuse to admit that the approach proper to physical science cannot show consciousness as a derivative of a biological structure. For self-consciousness is, by definition, internal self-experience and never a phenomenon that can be registered from without by physical science.[6]

The relationship between externally observable[7] structure and the manifestation of interiority, which is difficult even in the study of infra-human life, offers even more difficulties in the biological studies of man himself. A clear sign of the powerlessness of the method of physical science in this respect is that the paleobiologist, when he wants to determine whether bone fossils are human or not, lets himself be guided by the presence or absence of cultural remains. He has no other criterion. Which remains are men we determine primarily from manifestations of human culture and not from a biological structure. We can simply register as a fact that all human beings are, biologically speaking, closely related; therefore, we regard them as biologically belonging to one and the same species. But we do not have any insight allowing us to say that man as a rational animal must necessarily have the structure of the *homo sapiens*.[8] Thus there are two problems here. First, Are all animals possessing the biological structure of the *homo sapiens* of necessity human beings in the sense of *subjects* endowed with self-consciousness? Secondly,

---

[6]This statement does not at all mean that we are unable to know our fellow-men, for the recognition of our fellow-men does not take place through a scientific registration of an external phenomenon, but by way of human contact. On the other hand, correspondences also play an important role in this recognition. I recognize externally the human form and know then that I am dealing with a human being.

[7]We may emphasize again here that in this context the term "externally observable" includes all the techniques of observation and experimentation which penetrate into the "interior" and thereby exteriorize the interior and make it observable. Cf. van Melsen, *Science and Technology,* Pittsburgh, 1961, Ch. II, pp. 27 f.

[8]We take the term *homo sapiens* here in a broad sense, so that it can also include possible secondary branches that may have died out. The terminology in this matter has not yet been definitively fixed. Cf. B. Campbell, "The Systematics of Man." *Nature,* vol. 194 (1962), pp. 225-232.

Are self-conscious *subjects* with an entirely different biological structure possible?[9]

A modicum of guidance for the answering of these questions is at our disposal. For instance, it is evident that in man, as we know him, the biological structure, especially of the brain, is essential to being-a-subject. This leaves little to say in favor of dualistic theories which imply the indwelling of a spirit in man's body in a way that makes the kind of body in question almost irrelevant. But even so, there remains a whole spectrum of possibilities, in which at their present stage neither the theory of evolution nor biology in general can offer much guidance. At the same time it also remains uncertain what guidance these two can offer in the future, after developing their own program. We will return to this matter after seeing first what guidance philosophy can offer.

3. PHILOSOPHICAL REFLECTION AND MAN

As noted previously, there exists no unanimous philosophical view about man, and for this reason the reaction of philosophy to the theory of evolution is likewise characterized by diversity. This lack of unanimity, however, does not mean that philosophy is irrelevant to our problem. On the contrary, from its discussions one becomes aware of the issues involved in the theory of evolution.

Were there only a materialistic trend of philosophy, the evolutionary theory would not raise any philosophical problems. Since the theory would simply refer to the differentiation and complexification of material structures, their explanation could be left entirely to physical science. It is undoubtedly to the historical credit of materialism that it took matter seriously and later did the same with physical science; but it was unable to solve the problem of interiority and human self-consciousness. Classical materialism spoke about interiority and self-consciousness as "epiphenomena" and, by thus regarding them as phenomena of secondary rank, tried to minimize their importance. This procedure, however, was unsuccessful. As a reflective science, philosophy was too strongly geared to man's thinking to dismiss thinking as an "epiphenomenon," an incidental resultant of the material structure.

---

[9]In such questions the problem of correspondence becomes acute. It could very well be that to answer them one would have to go beyond the method of correspondence. Provisionally, however, it is not clear how one can go beyond this method.

Resistance to materialism arose early in ancient Greek philosophy when Socrates, Plato and Aristotle objected to Democritus' attempt to explain everything by atomic motion. Plato especially played an important role in this opposition. From an analysis of human knowledge Plato concluded that knowledge is more than a mere mirroring of spatio-temporal reality. Man's concepts, both mathematical and ethical, he argued, refer to perfections that are never encountered in experience. Hence these concepts, as well as the human being who possessed them, had to originate from a different and more perfect world. That which was most proper to man and constituted his inmost essence had to be a pure spirit transcending the limitations of space and time. While living on the perishable and changeable earth, the natural abode of the body, it was man's task to rediscover the imperishable and supraworldly reality of the perfect world, the world of ideas. In this way Plato arrived unhesitatingly at a dualistic conception of man: Man consists of a spiritual soul and a material body.

Aristotle mitigated this dualism by postulating a much more intimate union between soul and body. The soul is the "form" of the body, that is, it makes the matter of the body be a human body. It follows from this relationship that the soul would wholly perish with the body, but Aristotle did not want to accept this consequence. He admitted that the *nous,* the purely spiritual element of the soul, was eternal. By trying to stress both the unity of man and his spiritual aspect, Aristotle failed to make himself clear, but practically speaking, he arrived at a trichotomy of man: *soma* or body, *psyche* or soul, and *nous* or spirit. Since body and soul are internally related, the ultimate result is nonetheless a kind of dualism between a besouled body and a spirit.

As we have pointed out in the preceding chapters, the sharp opposition between spirit and matter in Greek thought was partially the result of the state of science in their era. For their time was characterized by the fact that the spirit could place itself at a distance from reality through its cognitive power while the body was powerless to interfere with the same reality.

Through the influence of St. Augustine, who had been educated in the neo-Platonic tradition, the dualistic idea became dominant in the Christian view of man. True, body and soul were no longer considered in direct opposition since both were viewed as created by God, but their relationship to the Creator was not the same. The soul was *immediately* created by God; but the body belonged to material reality and, therefore, was merely a part of the whole of creation; thus it originated through natural causes.

The view of St. Thomas Aquinas on the relationship of body and soul is especially interesting. Here, as in many other questions, he built a bridge between Plato and Aristotle. With Aristotle he held that the soul is the form of the body, but for Aquinas the term "soul" refers not only to the *psyche* but also to the *nous*. He admitted only one soul in man, the spiritual soul; it made the body a human body and therefore fulfilled the functions of the vegetative and sensitive souls, as well as that which was proper to a spiritual soul. This one spiritual soul was, in the full sense of the terms, both "form of the body" and subsistent. This Thomistic thesis has a twofold sense. In Thomistic thought the spirit is essentially an embodied spirit, it is not a pure spirit but a spirit which essentially seeks to impart itself to a body, to become embodied. At the same time, however, the body is "spiritualized," the body also is spirit "but in the mode of corporeity."[10]

Thomas Aquinas presented a series of impressive arguments to prove that the two theses were unified in his formula. For our purpose the important point of these arguments is the way in which he defended the soul's subsistence; for, he based his arguments for the soul's intrinsic independence of the body on the immateriality of the intellect's act of knowing.[11]

It is hardly necessary to add that Aquinas maintained the idea of the soul's direct creation. He could hardly have done otherwise, for the soul, as form of the body, made the body be a spiritualized human body. Thus it was necessary to raise the question of the soul's origin and this could not be answered with a reference to man's bodily origin. Bodily origin from the parents could at most explain that matter was rendered disposed to receive a spirit, but not the origin of this spirit itself. True, the parents themselves were spiritualized bodily beings; but since the spirit was precisely not a biological entity, it could not be produced by a natural biological process.

In Aquinas there was, of course, no question of thinking along evolutionary lines.[12] We may even add that, in the light of the

---

[10]Cf. E. Schillebeeckx, "De christelijke benadering van de menselijke lichamelijkheid," *Het centrale zenuwstelsel, symposionverslag medische faculteit,* Nijmegen, 1959, Ch. XIII, p. 3.

[11]Cf., e.g., *Summa theologica,* p. I, q. 75 and 76.

[12]Cf. N. Luyten, "Philosophical Implications of Evolution," *The New Scholasticism,* vol. 24 (1951), pp. 290-312.

preceding sketch of his ideas, he would have rejected a theory of integral evolution. Since the soul "forms" the body, evolution could at most refer to the biological preparation of man's coming to be. But even then there would have been serious objections because of the powerlessness of matter.

Although Aquinas fundamentally rejected dualism in man but maintained the distinction between matter and spirit, dualism staged a surprising come-back at the beginning of the seventeenth century. This resurgence was due to the influence of Descartes and his distinction between *res cogitans,* the thinking reality of the spirit, and *res extensa,* the material reality. At first this dualism sustained itself on the prevailing spirit of rationalism; but, when rationalism began to wane, dualism also lost much of its attractiveness. The development of philosophy as well as science contributed to the diminished credit of both rationalism and dualism.

To begin with science, as we have seen, its development was influential in two ways, namely, by its discoveries about man as object and by its findings about man as subject. Concerning man as object, science became increasingly more certain that it had to assume man's descent from the animal kingdom, but it did not limit itself to this historical point. All kinds of human sciences, such as psychology and sociology, took their orientation from biology and discovered constantly more striking relationships between man and animal;[13] and the medical sciences came to the conclusion that the sharp distinction between mental illness and bodily illness could no longer be maintained. With respect to man as subject there were likewise several important discoveries. One interests us here especially because it is concerned with a point that has always played an important role in tradition, namely, the intrinsic independence of intellectual knowledge from materiality. The development of physical science into an experimental science showed to what extent man's progress in knowledge depended intrinsically on bodily activity. This discovery undermined both dualism and rationalism.

Regarding the influence which the development of philosophy exercised on man's idea of man, let us begin by remarking that this influence should not be divorced from that exercised by the development of science. Since the seventeenth century, the evolution of philosophical thought has proceeded under the direct influence

---

[13]Cf., e.g., W. H. Thorpe, *Biology and the Nature of Man,* Oxford, 1962, Chapters II and III.

of the above-mentioned development of physical science. It could hardly avoid this influence, especially when one considers that the modern period saw the rise of positivism as one of the most important trends of philosophy. For the philosophical credo of positivism states that knowledge of reality can be obtained only by way of the positive sciences.

On the other hand it is also true that, especially in the modern period, philosophy began to lead a life of its own, more or less separately from the pursuit of science, and with its own problematics. Nevertheless, sometimes it owed its problems directly to the state of science at a particular time; in other words, philosophy considered problems that had arisen in close contact with science, but developed them on its own. A good example is provided by the epistemological problem as it was raised by Kant. The state of physical science led Kant to formulate this problem; but since that time it has led a life of its own, more or less independently of the development of physical science into experimental science and independently also of the development of technology. The same has happened to many other problems. In some circles, moreover, the philosophical problematics remained in direct contact with that of antiquity or the Middle Ages. For these reasons it is important to consider not only the direct influence which the development of science has exercised on our image of man, but also to ask about the way in which this image has been affected by the evolution of philosophical thought.

When we consider how philosophy has thought about man since Descartes, we notice immediately that in this era man is spoken of especially as a subject. At first this subject was conceived, particularly in the rationalistic and idealistic trends, as a spiritual subject and regarded as *pure* consciousness. As soon, however, as the dualistic tendencies began to wane, there was no longer any reason to conceive this pure consciousness as the consciousness of a spirit. Why, it was argued, should not this pure consciousness be the consciousness of man as the unification of spirit and matter?

Maurice Merleau-Ponty, for example, speaks explicitly of the body as subject. For, prior to all consciousness, the body is already oriented to the world and the world to the body. The world is full of meanings for the body, and explicit consciousness must therefore accept these meanings as more primordial than those which this consciousness itself gives to things. The conviction that the subject is not a thinking subject *in* a body but an embodied subject, exhibiting all the essential characteristics of embodied being, is widely accepted in contemporary philosophy, especially in the phenomenological and existential trends of thought.[14]   In some respects this view comes close to that of Thomas Aquinas, for whom the spirit was likewise an embodied spirit.   There remains, however, a great difference, since St. Thomas attributed primacy to the spirit as embodying itself and becoming embodied spirit, while for contemporary philosophers there is no question of giving priority to the spirit.   They do not conceive man as a spirit which has embodied itself, as a spirit which has formed a body, but state that man is equiprimordially body and spirit.[15]

At first it could seem that the contemporary view of man offers few difficulties for the acceptance of the theory of evolution because man's bodiliness occupies such an important place in this view. Closer inspection, however, shows that this bodiliness is not the body as it is studied by the biologist.   The contemporary view is concerned with the body as subject, as an essential aspect of man as embodied spirit.   The body subject is not a body whose origin one can investigate but is itself origin.   This term "origin" is not understood in the sense of creating the world but in the sense that the body is an "original," primordial, orientation to the world, so that the world is meaningful to the body.   For this reason Alphonse de Waelhens points out that the human body is essentially different from any animal body.   He rejects therefore the definition of man as a rational animal because this definition assumes that the human body and the animal body are generically the same.[16]

This irreducible primordial character of man as a subject, as an "existence" for which things are there, expresses itself perhaps most sharply in the phenomenological view of positive human sciences. As we have mentioned above, there is a way of looking at these sciences as prolongations of biology, so that data of animal psychology and animal sociology are regarded as offering a basis for the psychology and sociology of man.   According to the phenomenological standpoint, however, animal sciences and human sciences are essen-

---

[14]Cf. Remy C. Kwant, *The Phenomenological Philosophy of Merleau-Ponty,* Pittsburgh, 1962, and William A. Luijpen, *Existential Phenomenology,* Pittsburgh, 4th impr., 1965.

[15]For a critical comparison of the thomistic and the phenomenological views of man, see N. Luyten, "De betekenis van het lichaam in een thomistische antropologie," *Tijdschrift voor Filosofie,* vol. 25 (1963), pp. 3-37.

[16]*La philosophie et les expériences naturelles,* The Hague, 1961, Ch. VIII.

tially separated because, in the case of man, all actions are actions of an "existent" subject. No matter how much the animal, biologically speaking, may be an individual subject, this subject is never an "existent" subject, a subject which illumines reality because it is a light to itself. True, even man as subject is not a pure spirit, a perfect light to himself. Man is a spirit which as embodied spirit is essentially limited, so that all light is at the same time permeated with darkness. Nevertheless, man's self-consciousness, his knowing about himself which permeates all actions of this subject, is not taken away by this limitation, for this subject knows at least about that light and that darkness. Expressed without the symbolism of light and darkness, the subject is aware of its limitations.

Man's awareness of his own limitations is the point that can be used here in an effort to penetrate deeper into the philosophical problematics of the evolutionary theory. First, however, a few remarks about the multitude of philosophical views recorded in the preceding pages are needed. It would not do to dismiss philosophy entirely, alleging that its divisions manifest its uselessness. For this very division reveals the true dimensions of the problem raised by the issue of evolution. Moreover, no reflection upon the theory of evolution has ever benefited by disregarding the distances which the theory wants to bridge, viz., those that separate matter, life, and spirit.

If, for example, one eliminates that which is proper to man, he eliminates at the same time the problem of evolution with respect to man. Undoubtedly, it is necessary to rethink the relationship between matter, life, and spirit in the perspective of the evolutionary theory, but such a rethinking should not begin by removing the real tension between these three. No matter how related man and animal are, reflection upon human existence, upon man as a subject, neutralizes this relationship.

Thus it appears that the choice of a philosophical perspective *de facto* determines the answer to the question of evolution. One who begins with man as a subject seems irrevocably to close the road to evolution, even if he takes the bodiliness of man as a subject seriously. His standpoint opens an unbridgeable gap between man and everything else. On the other hand, one who starts with the inner relationship between all material beings, as it is presupposed by physical science, has no difficulty in accepting evolution but cuts himself off from any possibility of ever reaching man.

Unless one dismisses philosophy as irrelevant because of its divisions, only one conclusion can be drawn from all this: the various philosophical views are partial truths and must be taken together to reach the truth. This "taking together" does not consist, of course, in simply adding one to another; different philosophical trends of thinking can no more be added to one another than can different sciences. With respect to the sciences, the impossibility of adding one to the other offers no particular problem. For we know that each science has its own way of approaching reality, each has its own truth; these different truths therefore are not in direct contradiction. Man knows that the limitations of his knowledge force him to use different approaches; hence he realizes that to eliminate these differences by an attempted synthesis would mean that he does not attach much importance to his limitations.

The various sciences are, as it were, distinct ways along which man's single desire for truth tries to advance. The one grasp for the truth which was Greek philosophy has, so to speak, become spatialized in the juxtaposed graspings for reality of the many sciences. The same Greek grasp has also become temporalized, in the sense that all sciences develop. This spatialization and temporalization mirrors the fact that the human spirit is not a pure spirit but an embodied spirit. Thus it can be seen that the sciences are to some extent embodiments of the one original philosophical impulse.

As we have seen, however, philosophy has not simply dissolved into the various sciences, but retains a function of its own. Philosophy remains the unifying element in the plurality of sciences, but it cannot fulfill this function in a way which would eliminate this plurality. A sign of this "powerlessness" of philosophy is the fact that there are many philosophies. They extend the diversity of the sciences to the philosophical level, where the division is felt much more keenly because here the differences are of a contradictory nature. They are concerned with the same level of thought.[17] However, no matter how painful the philosophical division is, this division itself, as we have said, gives expression to the fact that man is aware of his limitation. He knows that he is still far from having reached the goal and must continue thinking along many avenues of approach.

Accordingly, the philosopher should realize that any philosophical approach is only an approach and he should be resigned to the fact that he cannot encompass everything in a single grasp. He must

---

[17]This problem will be discussed more fully in Ch. 9, Section 2.

have the courage to gather together in his thinking, to the best of his ability, many philosophical avenues of thought, whether or not they have originated in close contact with science, even though he knows that this attempt cannot yet be realized and perhaps will never fully succeed. Yet he can retain his hope for the future because he has experienced the dynamism of his thinking as one of its most essential aspects.

4. MATTER, LIFE, AND SPIRIT

A philosophical consideration of matter, life, and spirit can be fruitful only if one remains aware of the various trends of thought indicated in the preceding section and the results to which they have led. At the same time there must be a recognition that each of these trends is bound to have certain limitations. Yet the attempt to look philosophically at matter, life, and spirit will find many encouraging signs. The development of physical science, for example, shows that matter possesses much more activity of its own than was first held possible. For this way the fundamental idea of materialism loses something of its unacceptability, even for those who want first and foremost to place full emphasis on the special value of life and especially of man. At any rate, the development of physical science has resulted in a greater understanding of the phenomena of life. These phenomena appear to flow from the complexity of the material structures present in the organism.

Meanwhile the main difficulty continues to lie in interiority. Despite the success of physical science in explaining vital phenomena, interiority remains the big stumbling block. Yet even here there is some encouragement to go on. If there were no interiority whatsoever in the realm of life prior to man, so that in him interiority would at once assume the form of self-consciousness, then any theory of evolution that includes man would face an impossible task. The gap between man and non-human forms of life would be insurmountable.

Another encouraging factor is that the human subject is not only a spiritual-corporeal subject but also a subject that as subject has not yet fully realized itself. The human subject grows in its being a subject. To use the most evident example, self-consciousness is certainly not a property of a human embryo or newborn infant. This, of course, does not bridge the gap between material structure and spirit, but at least this gap does not appear unbridgeable from the very start. Somehow, the gap is bridged in reality. And almost spontaneously we wonder whether, perhaps, part of our difficulties in merging matter and spirit does not arise from our own way of thinking and speaking.

To answer this, it seems worthwhile to critically investigate the way we usually speak about the scale of nature. We distinguish inorganic things, living beings,[18] and man; and attribute the same material being to living beings as to inorganic things, save for the addition of the distinguishing characteristic of life. This way of speaking suggests that living beings possess so-called "life" in addition to material being. "Life" is, as it were, substantialized and the living being is regarded as matter with the additive of life. To the being of matter one adds the distinguishing feature of life, making the whole a living being. The same process is repeated with man. Man is regarded as a living being in which being-a-spirit is a kind of external additive. This way of looking at man manifests itself in his classical definition as "rational animal": man is a living being, an animal, to which rationality has been added.

This manner of speaking in terms of additions is not without consequences. If man is a rational animal, then the "ordinary" animal is, of course, non-rational. If a plant or an animal is a living being, then the material being is, of course, non-living. In this way living and non-living, rational and non-rational are placed in contradictory opposition. This applies also to material and spiritual; spiritual means immaterial and material means non-spiritual.

Considered in itself, this way of speaking is not wrong, provided we do not uncritically draw conclusions that flow from the way of speaking rather than from that which is spoken of. For speaking about matter as non-spiritual suggests that in the material being there is nothing that has anything in common with the spiritual. The same applies to the distinction between living and non-living. The suggestion in question easily leads us to substantialize the spiritual and the living, to regard them as independent entities or principles added from without as something entirely new to pre-existing realities. As a matter of fact, vitalism fell into this trap with respect to the realm of the living and dualism slipped into it with regard to man. We do not mean to say, of course, that these consequences follow only from that way of speaking and of manipulating logical concepts. Nevertheless, the ease with which this way of speaking leads to these consequences should put us on guard.

---

[18]We abstract here from the distinction between vegetative and sensitive life.

We must, therefore, ask ourselves critically in what sense it can be meaningful to speak of "life," "principle of life," and "spirit." First, we experience "life" only in the form of material living beings. Outside this form "life" does not exist, at least as far as our experience can determine. This fact should make us pause to think, for it indicates that there must be a special relationship between what we call *life* and *material reality*. If *life* does not exist outside matter, it can hardly be an extrinsic addition to matter but should rather be regarded as a special mode of being of matter.

Can we make the same statements regarding spirit? An affirmative reply seems to be rather obvious, yet we hesitate to draw a parallel conclusion. For, unlike what happens in the case of life, man speaks of "pure spirits."[19] Strange as it may seem, although we speak of "pure spirits," we experience only spiritual aspects of man but never spiritual beings existing outside the human world. Why, then, do we speak of *pure* spirits? The reason cannot lie solely in the careless use of language, for otherwise we would also be likely to speak of "pure life" on an infraspiritual but nonetheless supramaterial level. The only possible reason seems to be that our human experiences contain indications pointing to purely spiritual reality.

The principal indication would appear to be the fact that man experiences the limitation of his own being-spiritual, which expresses itself in his self-consciousness and his freedom. We may even say that man's awareness of his own limitation is what is most of all expressed by the concept "spirit." "Spirit" expresses the transcendental openness which overcomes all limitation by being aware of the limitation. Nevertheless, this transcendence is of a peculiar nature because it is, as it were, indirect; it is experienced only in the awareness that knowledge is limited and not in a vision lying beyond all limitation. The indirect character of this transcendence is manifest also in the way in which man is present to himself. Man's self-presence, his being with himself, is somehow indirect because it is experienced in man's being-a-subject, i.e., in a cognitive activity which is not primarily directed to itself but co-experienced in man's intentional directedness to the object. In other words, man experiences even his self-presence as limited.

---

[19]These "pure spirits" also are said to *live,* but this life is not life in the biological sense of the term. For this reason our remarks about "pure life" remain valid.

Because of his transcendence, man suspects that this limitation and indirectness of his self-presence are not characteristic of self-presence as such but only of human self-presence. He ascribes the limitation to the embodied character of his spirit, which has to come to itself by cognitively going out to things and co-discovering itself, in the process, as the subject that goes out to the things. But if limitation is characteristic only of man's self-presence, then we have not excluded the possibility that there exist subjects who are fully "with themselves," subjects that are pure spirits because their being-spiritual is not dependent upon bodily limitations. This line of thought, of course, does not prove the existence of pure spirits, but at most that such spirits are possible.

Generally speaking, however, the existence of pure spirits did not constitute a problem in traditional philosophy. As we have seen, Aristotle concluded to their existence from the order of the cosmos. Material things, he argued, act in an orderly fashion, they tend to their natural end without knowing the end; therefore, they must be guided by separate substances, which he conceived as pure spirits. Insofar as physical science in a later stage of development no longer needed these spirits to govern the things of nature, there is every reason to doubt the truth of this Aristotelian view. Nevertheless, reality as a whole, both natural and human, was still as limited as ever. For this reason the question of pure spirits culminated, after centuries of discussion, in the problem whether the limited did not point to something unlimited, to the fullness of being, the source and origin of all beings. This fullness of being at least would have to be a kind of pure spirit, enjoying full self-presence. If something could be affirmed of God, it would be at least that He is a pure spirit.

Man's attempt to think about God obviously touches the limits of his possibilities and therefore constantly raises the question whether he can really attain the desired goal[20] or, for instance, whether God is merely a projection of what man would like to be, based on man's own view of himself. At any rate, the more man understands himself, the more he realizes that he must amend his image of God.[21] Yet one cannot *a priori* say that man's progressive self-understanding automatically makes God superfluous, for the mystery of man's existence increases in direct ratio to his growth in self-understanding, through the results achieved by the sciences and philosophical reflec-

[20]Cf. the quotation of G. G. Simpson on page 76.
[21]Cf. William A. Luijpen, *Phenomenology and Atheism*, Pittsburgh, 1965.

tion upon these results. The more his knowledge grows, the more man experiences both his grandeur and his limitations. The question regarding the absolute origin remains, although it becomes less easy to grasp. We will return to this point later in connection with another problem. It has been raised here only because we asked the question whether it is meaningful to speak of "pure spirits" on the basis of man's self-experience. From the preceding pages it follows that this question must be answered in the affirmative.

This reply, however, is not yet a positive answer to the question that concerns us most in this section, namely, must man's being-spiritual be regarded as an addition to his bodiliness, either in an extremely dualistic sense or in the sense of "embodied spirit"? Thus far we have only observed that it can be meaningful to speak of a "pure spirit" and that therefore the dualistic view does not have to be rejected as foundationless on the basis that one of the supposed "components" of the dualistic composite cannot possibly exist. The conclusion that such a rejection is not justified does not, of course, imply any positive argument in favor of the dualistic view.

Whether man's being-spiritual must be regarded as an extrinsic addition or an internal unfolding of matter is a point that is not yet definitively answered by the preceding pages. We must now devote our attention to this. In this investigation it could perhaps become clear that the dualistic view, at least in its moderate form, is not only a possible view but the only possible view because all other views of man could appear to be untenable. If being-alive and being-spiritual are not based on extrinsic additions to matter but constitute its internal unfoldings, then they must be contained in some incipient way in material being. That which manifests itself later must be previously present in an incipient way.

This general statement applies to both the philosophical and the scientific way of approaching reality. Physical science, however, can limit itself to showing that the structures of inorganic material being are, in an incipient way, the structures of the living organism with their manifold of complexifications. Philosophy, on the other hand, must investigate whether material being contains a capacity for spiritual being. If the answer to the philosophical question is in the negative, then some form of dualism will be inevitable.

In this investigation everything will depend, of course, on the way one defines the material and the spiritual. If they are simply defined as mutually exclusive, the question is settled at once. But is it right to define them in that fashion? Undoubtedly, it is true that man experiences the material as the limitation of his self-presence and freedom. While he knows that he is a material structure, he is not present from within in the functioning of this structure. Strictly speaking, his self-presence is limited, so to speak, to the culmination points of his existence, his so-called spiritual acts of knowing and willing. His biological and material activities, however, largely lie beyond his internal self-knowledge. What man knows about the functioning of his bodily being he learns only by studying it through physical science. The biological functioning of the body is known to man only as an "object."

All this, then, seems to indicate the essential opacity from within that is proper to matter, even in the case of one's own bodily being. The view, therefore, which opposes the material to the spiritual is based on real grounds. Yet the question remains whether these grounds are sufficiently convincing.

First of all, the body manifests itself not only as opposed to the spirit. For the body is also subject. In our self-experience we experience that the body situates our being-a-subject not only negatively as a limitation to the here and now but also positively as opening up possibilities for man. By being situated in the here and now, we are at the same time orientated in material reality. Perhaps the matter could be expressed in this way: for a pure spirit, embodiment—if it were possible—would mean only limitation; but for a spirit which from the very beginning is related to the world, embodiment is precisely the way to express this relationship. We are touching here an essentially difficulty implied in any extremely dualistic conception of man: Does it make any sense to speak about the embodiment of a pure spirit?

If the human spirit pre-existed as a pure immaterial spirit, entirely independent of the body, what possible meaning could be attached to its embodiment? Any meaning would have to be found in the interplay of this spirit with the body. But such an interplay is conceivable only if we were to regard this spirit as somehow embodied. Only a spirit that is already embodied would be able, by way of its own bodiliness, to govern that which we call the body, for bodily organs are needed to govern the body. If they were not needed, if the spirit could do without such organs, then its embodiment would be utterly meaningless. For this reason extreme dualism appears to be untenable.

The rejection of extreme dualism leads to the position occupied by Thomas Aquinas: the spirit is the "form" of the body; it is essentially one with the body and nonetheless subsistent, not totally encompassed by the body. The Thomistic position harmonizes very well with our own self-experience. Our thinking is of necessity embodied in words, but is it really true, as Merleau-Ponty suggests, that it is wholly encompassed by words?[22] Man's thinking always retains a certain independence with respect to every expression, precisely because it knows that every expression is inadequate. True, it can never overcome this inadequacy, which shows the limiting character of embodiment. It can even never express this inadequacy in any other way than in other inadequate expressions, which shows the necessity of embodiment. Yet throughout every expression, man's thinking is aware of this inadequacy, which points to a certain autonomy. This autonomy Aquinas expressed by the term "subsistent."

The formula used by Thomas Aquinas is also, of course, inadequate, but nonetheless to the point. The question now is what exactly the consequences of this formula are. And, among these consequences, which ones must be attributed to the inadequacy of the expression and which to the ideas expressed in his formula? Does it follow from the formula that the spirit enjoys such a priority over the body that there could be no evolution from the material to the spiritual? In other words, does the coming to be of man mean, of necessity, to receive a spirit?

To avoid misunderstandings, let us point out at once that even an affirmative reply to this question can be fully in harmony with the tenets of the evolutionary theory. For, the precise nature of hominization lies beyond man's powers of perception. The theory of evolution can say, at most, that at a given time and in a given place an animal developed into man. Anyone aware of the fundamental change implied in hominization realizes that the possibility of considering the coming to be of man as the infusion of a spirit suggests itself here very forcefully. For this reason it would be wrong to attribute the thesis of the special creation of the human soul, which even Teilhard maintained, simply to conformism with Christian dogma. From a purely philosophical standpoint, too, there are great difficulties in any other thesis.

---

[22]*Phenomenology of Perception,* New York, 1962, pp. 174-199.

Nevertheless, it cannot be denied that the thesis of the soul's special creation can easily be suspected of being introduced merely to bridge the embarrassing gap between man and animal. In one respect at least this is certainly the case, because in that respect the thesis really solves nothing. To speak more clearly, the thesis is too general, for it does not explain why precisely this *particular* bodily being became man. And, in this respect the thesis resembles the well-known Aristotelian thesis, taken over by Aquinas, explaining the "fact" that eels come to be from mud by an appeal to the universal causality of the sun. Mud, it was admitted, had the capacity to become an eel; but it alone could not actualize this capacity, for that would have been against the philosophical principle that "nothing can pass from potency to act save under the influence of something that is in act." This principle and its validity will be discussed later. Presently we merely wish to remark that recourse to the sun, which as a celestial body was supposedly sufficiently "in act" to serve as cause, was meaningless, at least in the sense that this appeal did not at all explain why eels came to be precisely from mud. Why not buttercups instead of eels and why no eels from sandstone?

Accordingly, this useless appeal to the sun simply repeats the original principle in a camouflaged form. It does not give any explanation. A similar criticism applies to the thesis that the human soul originates from a special creation. It does not really explain anything because it can be used to explain everything. A genuine explanation of the transformation of an animal into man has to be borne by the insight that matter can become living, that in the realm of the living the animal can develop, and that the animal can become man on the basis of an inherent capacity.

From the philosophical standpoint, therefore, the crucial problem is twofold. We must show that being-spiritual exists in capacity in matter and we must show the way in which this capacity can be realized. To what extent an appeal has to be made to creation is another question, which should be raised only later. To raise this question prematurely not only generates confusion in the scientific and philosophical problems involved in the matter of evolution, but also places it in danger of becoming itself confused with other questions.

To seek in material reality for the capacity of everything that subsequently develops from it means, briefly put, this: we must try to see evolution not as a development in which something is constantly added from without to the preceding phase, but as an inner unfolding to which matter is oriented from the very beginning. In this way matter retains its character of limitation, mentioned above, but this limitation now knows grades and no longer stands in contradictory opposition to spirit. Let us begin with this last point.

Material being is never in total contradictory opposition to the knowing spirit because material being is at least knowable. One could object that knowability is something passive while knowing is precisely something active; but this objection is not valid since, with respect to knowing, there is no question of opposing the purely active to the purely passive. The knowability of the material being should not be conceived as something purely passive. The simple fact that our knowledge of material reality depends upon experiments shows that this knowability also contains the active aspect of *making* itself known. This way of speaking is not a mere metaphor, for it is precisely by its *activity* that material reality makes itself known.

On the other hand, the fact that man's knowledge depends upon the activity of material reality indicates that his knowing is not purely active. We do not simply mean that knowing has the passive aspect of being dependent upon things in their concrete being, for in this sense passivity would merely mean that man's knowing does not create reality but only understands the reality which it encounters. Passivity here refers to an aspect of knowledge which, at least within the realm of scientific knowledge, has revealed itself only since the birth of physical science. It means that only the varied activity of things, as disclosed by the experiment, makes our growing knowledge of them possible. This passive aspect manifests itself not only in our knowledge of *material* reality, but also—be it indirectly—in man's self-knowledge, as we have seen in the preceding chapters.

All this, of course, does not eliminate the fundamental difference between man and thing. Only man *knows,* the thing is merely know*able.* The fundamental difference between active self-knowledge and passive being-known is preserved; yet there is also an inner relationship so pervasive that knowing is not pure activity and being-known not pure passivity.

In this way we arrive at the next step in our consideration of the relationship existing between beings. Until now our attention has been devoted mainly to the role which the activity of material beings plays in the cognitive process. The point to be studied right now is material activity itself. In our previous discussion this activity played a role as an active aspect of the process of cognition, and this role, considered from the part of the material things, seemed to point only to passivity manifesting itself in the knowability of these things.

The problem now concerns the significance of the subordinate and essentially passive role which material beings play in the cognitive process. Is this role subordinate only in the sense that it appears to be subordinate whenever it is regarded as an aspect of the cognitive process, or is its subordinate character proper to material activity as such? The reply to this question which we propose may be presented in a twofold thesis: 1. The ontological level of a being corresponds to the level of its activity; 2. This level finds expression in the role which this activity plays with respect to cognition. Differently expressed, if we ascribe to material beings only a very relative, though real, active role in a cognitive process in which otherwise they are passive, then this same relativity also applies to their activity in general.

This thesis, of course, must be substantiated. As we have seen in Chapter Three, the initially predominant view which did not attribute any activity of its own to the material being—unless living—has been antiquated by the development of physical science. Material beings also have activities of their own. In spite of the truth of this statement, this activity remains permeated with passivity. Material beings undergo their activity at least as much as they exercise it; this is the ultimate meaning of the determinism of material beings. They do not determine their own activity, but their activity is wholly anchored in their proper character. There can be question of "own" activity in the strict sense only where there exists self-knowledge, that is, where activity is free activity, an activity coming from the acting being itself. In other words, the level of activity and that of knowledge are intimately attuned to each other and at the same time express the level of being. The highest level of being is that of self-presence, in which a being exists at the same time for itself; to this corresponds a level of activity in which there is question of a being's own activity because it is this being's known activity.

Against the background of these considerations it is meaningful not to view the "scale of nature" as a ladder in which each level is characterized by the extrinsic addition of something new but as a graded internal unfolding of something already there, though this something may manifest itself through this unfolding in a totally new way. This idea means that the human level of being is not essentially again the same level as that of material beings, so that the specifically human element would arise from the spirit that is also present on this human level; on the contrary, man's being-spiritual is precisely the expression of the new level of being itself.

Similar considerations apply to life with the various grades it contains. Being-alive expresses the specific level of being of the material being in question. And, within the realm of life, the cognitive level of a being expresses at the same time its level of being. One could surmise that this remark is added simply as a corollary, since in the preceding pages we emphasized almost exclusively the opposition between material being and man. In a certain sense this impression is correct. It was certainly not by accident that we left non-human living reality provisionally out of consideration. Part of the reason was that, with respect to the interpretation of the "scale of nature" as the unfolding of being, the extremes to be bridged demand more attention than the intermediaries. But there was another reason of a more fundamental nature: it is much easier to speak about the respective ontological levels of man and material beings than of those of plants and animals.

This fact is connected with the rather strange phenomenon that man's knowledge can, at least apparently, reach the extremes more easily. He reaches himself by way of reflection upon his own activity, to which he is present from within in his self-consciousness. And he reaches material beings by way of sense knowledge going out to external things. But how is he to reach living reality? He will have to do it either through his "outgoing" sense knowledge, as it is refined especially in physical science, or by way of his reflective self-knowledge. In the former case plants and animals will appear to him only as complex material structures; in the latter, he will try to see them as he sees himself. In both cases he misses that which is proper to the living being. He has trouble assigning their proper place to them, as is evident from the problematics concerning the interiority of life.

Meanwhile this failure to grasp the living being in its own character should serve as a sign that there must also be something wrong with the way in which man himself and material being are attained. These too appear to be inadequately reached in their own character. It could hardly be otherwise as long as man is characterized as self-presence and freedom without any explicit mention of his bodiliness. Yet how difficult it is to insert this bodiliness is shown by contemporary philosophy. It places great emphasis upon man's bodily being, but the abyss between the consideration of the body as subject and the body as object remains. Material being, likewise, is not fully reached if we consider it in its activity only as this finds expression in the study which physical science performs.

These remarks do not neutralize what was said above about the various levels of being, yet they indicate that complementary considerations are necessary, so that life can find its proper place among these levels. This can only be done through the assumption that the interiority which manifests itself in the living, even on a non-human level, is intimately connected with the "externally" observable material organization. Somehow this organization must be essentially connected with the specific phenomena of consciousness. In this way one can understand why Teilhard de Chardin postulates that the non-living also must have a "within," although this "within" does not yet manifest itself on the inorganic level.

Teilhard's intention in this matter is to overcome the one-sidedness of physical science; but his terminology, especially when he speaks of two kinds of energy, makes one suspect that he wishes to ascribe different properties to the "within" and to the "without." Thus there arises a kind of "double" reality. Such a procedure seems to be fundamentally wrong and to be based on a kind of projection into reality of the two different cognitive attitudes man can assume. The substantialization of these two attitudes with respect to man leads to a dualistic view of man and can also lead to a dualistic conception of all reality.

Strange as it may seem, it is precisely the development of physical science which has clearly shown how much physical science as a cognitive activity is at the same time an activity of handling things, i.e., it is eminently a spiritual-material activity. It has therefore contributed to undermining the dualistic view of man, which consequently means that there can be no dualizing conception of non-human reality. If this is true, then neither non-living nor living beings have, in addition to their externally observable complexity with its laws and energies, an interiority with corresponding laws and energies. In other words, the observable complexity itself expresses something about the essence of the level of being in question.

Thus the scientific study of matter's ability to form larger complexes and eventually to form living organisms deals essentially with an inner tendency to interiority, or rather, this ability *is* that tendency insofar as the ability can be made observable by the methods of physical science. Phrased in yet another way, the scientific approach to a living organism studies in the relative autonomy manifesting itself in self-development and self-preservation interiority itself, as it appears—from the standpoint of physical science—on this ontological level, viz., the level of the plant, in which there seems to be no sensitivity, and that of the higher type of animal. In this study it becomes strikingly clear that the road to more interiority, and consequently to a more autonomous unity of being, appears to run by way of increasing complexification.

Another possibly significant point is that, as we deal with higher forms of life, a more pronounced autonomous individuality in the biological sense manifests itself in spite of the increasing complexification. This individuality reveals itself in a twofold way. On the one hand, the individuals are more clearly distinct as separate units from other units; this is manifested visibly by their enclosing skin cover. On the other, their own chemical structure has something which is characteristically individual. On lower levels of life these two features are lacking. On these levels "individuals" easily merge into a single new individual, and a single individual is easily divided into several. Transplantations from one individual to another likewise cause no problem here.[23] One could even say that sometimes such transplantations occur naturally. In this light it is legitimate to ask whether perhaps the individually different structure of each distinct individual's proteins is connected with the uniqueness of every higher type of being, as this uniqueness manifests itself in interiority.[24]

Man is not an exception to all this. On the contrary, just as interiority reaches its apex in him, so also does biological individuality. The dualistic view of man substantialized man's unity in the unity of his soul—to such an extent even that the soul was regarded as in no way whatsoever extended (Augustine, Thomas Aquinas, Descartes) lest man's unity be jeopardized. No matter, however, how real this unity is, it is *de facto,* even in man, a unity existing

---

[23]As, e.g., in grafting branches on a fruit tree.

[24]Cf. M. Jeuken, "The Concept 'Individual' in Biology," *Acta Biotheoretica,* vol. X (1952), pp. 57-86; P. B. Medawar, *The Uniqueness of the Individual,* London, 1957.

by way of a plurality. The unity of man's self-consciousness itself bears witness to that plurality, for it is a unity in plurality. (There is every reason to suppose that the unity of man does not arise from an externally added principle of unity but is a unity arising from within, which has its first feeble beginnings in any living organism.) How this unity arises and somehow exists in every living being is a question about which very little is known as yet.

For this reason the preceding remarks did not intend to answer that question, but only to show that matter and spirit are not so contradictorily opposed that in matter there cannot be present a capacity tending to spiritual being. The additional explanations were used to emphasize the fact that the realization of this capacity appears essentially connected with the complexification of the material structures into living structures, even though it remains true that we do not yet understand this essential connection.

There is one great difficulty in trying to understand the connection, and this difficulty can be considered an essential objection against the whole idea of the unfolding of being, as it has been developed above. This difficulty is that it is not at all clear why the unfolding of being, at certain points, assumes so much the character of a leap that it indicates the attainment of a new level of being. The two most important leaps here are from non-living to living and from animal to man. Why does the "scale of nature" reveal itself as relatively clear-cut realms of being and not in the form of an absolutely continuous whole of gradual unfoldings?[25] In the realms of plants and animals there is such a continuity, at least to a degree, so that the boundary between plant and animal becomes vague in the microcosmic world. There is no such continuity, however, between living and non-living, even though viruses may be regarded as a kind of no-man's-land between the two. Nevertheless, this difficulty should not be regarded as insurmountable for the simple reason that man still knows very little about the connection between observable complexity and the essence of the level of being. An increase in knowledge may be able to explain why only at certain points an essential change can occur.

At any rate, if we are right in assuming that observable complexity expresses something pertaining to the essence of the level

[25]Teilhard de Chardin also devotes attention to this question. Cf. *The Phenomenon of Man*, Bk. II, Ch. I, Sect. 1, and Bk. III, Ch. I, Sect. 1 (in Torchbook ed., pp. 79 ff. and 164 ff.).

of being, it follows that the study of the various levels of being by way of the method of physical science is likely to be the only way in which the distinction between matter and life can be better understood. It also follows that by way of this apparently necessary detour we will be able to understand something more of man himself as spirit-in-matter. In this way man could grow in self-consciousness through his scientific activity and his philosophical reflection upon that activity, thus becoming more a light unto himself by means of these "outgoing" and "returning" activities. And perhaps this growing self-knowledge of man will also be of crucial importance for biology. Let us see why.

As explained above, one way in which the relativity of man's self-consciousness expresses itself is that man has no clear insight into his own material and vital structures. As a consequence of this lack of insight he cannot situate the interiority of living being in general. In speaking of interiority the biologist tacitly appeals, of course, to his self-experience; but precisely because this self-experience is deficient and lacks depth, this appeal also remains vague and without clarifying power.

On the other hand, the unsatisfactory situation prevailing in biology is an obstacle preventing man's clear understanding of himself. Everything here awaits a break-through, but it is not at all clear whether the break-through will come in the biology of plants, of animals or of man. The probability that it will come in the biology of man is favored by the fact that, in man, interiority is most manifest, so that here it is easier to observe the correspondences between scientific data and data of self-experience. Balanced against this is that with respect to man everything is so much more complicated from the standpoint of physical science. Yet no matter where the break-through comes, it appears certain that physical science will play a decisive role in it.

Only after this break-through, we think, will the theory of evolution be able to make essential progress. For the problem of explaining evolution is none other than the central problem of biology in general and of man in particular, namely, to understand how the material structures make vital and spiritual activities possible. One could perhaps be inclined to reject, in principle, the idea that physical science can make a decisive contribution to this question because the method of this science never grasps man in his specifically human character. Such a rejection may at first seem to safeguard man's eminent dignity, but on closer inspection it shows a lack of faith in the possibilities open to man. For such a rejection means *de facto* that man is permanently fixed on the rather poor level of self-knowledge and freedom that characterizes him at present.

These remarks are not intended to imply that it is *a priori* certain that a clarification coming from physical sicence will of necessity point in the direction of integral evolution. It is possible that such a clarification would show how inexplicable the passage from non-living to living remains, as well as that from animal to man. All we want to point out is that, if there is any hope of progress in this matter, physical science will play a decisive role in it. For this reason also we noted before that only physical science can decide whether abiogenesis is possible, and this question is obviously important for the distinction between living and non-living. On the other hand, this does not mean that this question pertains exclusively to physical science.

The idea that physical science can make a decisive contribution to the growth of man's self-consciousness likewise does not *per se* imply that man must be regarded as a product of evolution. Even if with respect to hominization one would have to think of the infusion of a spirit rather than the becoming-spiritual of material reality, it remains part of the spirit's task to understand itself and to see in what way it is bodily present and conditioned by its bodiliness in its expression. (Perhaps we may assume that the definitive reply to the problem of infusion of a spirit versus the becoming-spiritual of matter can be given only after the issue has been clarified by physical science.) Precisely because in modern times we have discovered that physical science is characterized by progressiveness, we should be prudent with *a priori* denials of possibilities. Moreover, is it not true that, even today, man's progressive knowledge and control of matter shows not so much that matter limits the spirit but rather that the limitation must be attributed to the immaturity of the human spirit? In this question one can leave provisionally undecided whether this immaturity refers to immaturity of becoming-spiritual or to immaturity of being-permeated with the spirit.

The discussion of the possibility that man becomes progressively more human will be reconsidered in one of the following chapters, after we have discussed several problems that are concerned with this hominization itself. If, as we have seen above, the "scale of nature" may be regarded as a progressive unfolding of being, then the philosophical difficulty that matter and spirit are essentially foreign to each other disappears; but it is not yet clear what driving forces lead to this unfolding. Who or what causes it? And more especially, how are the passages from one level to another, which are so evident in that unfolding, to be explained? These questions are connected with others, such as, whether or not evolution, conceived as unfolding, must be directed. And if the answer is in the affirmative, what kind of a directedness is this? These questions have presented themselves before in a more or less incidental way, but they have not yet been discussed here in a thorough way. To prepare that discussion, we must first reflect upon the problems of causality and finality.

CHAPTER SEVEN

CAUSALITY AND FINALITY

1. Historical Notes

The terms "causality" and "finality" carry a heavy historical burden. In many periods of history they were the center of wide-spread disputes, to such an extent that their history presents a mirror image of the history of philosophy and science. The two terms also play an important role in the history of biology, for one of the controverted points between mechanism and vitalism concerned the position to be assigned to the "final" explanation of life's phenomena. Mechanism held that all explanations should be causal, while vitalism claimed that, in addition to the causal factors, there was also a final element, incapable of being reduced to these causal factors because it made them subservient to itself.

By opting for a purely causal explanation, mechanism pursued the line chosen by physical science since the seventeenth century. In the old world view the order of nature had been interpreted as an order that was deliberately directed from without, but seventeenth century physical science began to interpret this order as somehing resulting from laws implied in the very nature of material reality. This change of view is often expressed as follows: with the development which began with the rise of physical science, the causal way of thinking replaced the final way. This expression, however, is not entirely correct, for it was inevitable that the development of science would make important changes in the very meaning of the terms "causality" and "finality."

In studying these changes of meaning, it will be necessary to make again the distinction which proved so useful in Chapter Three, namely, between explicit meaning and implicit meaning. The implicit development of meaning occurred through the function exercised by the category of causality in physical science. The explicit meaning is developed by way of philosophical reflection upon physical science and the insights achieved by this science. Here again it is striking how much richer the implicit functioning was than its explicitation. The implicit development of the concept "causality" was, of course, greatly stimulated when physical science acquired new aspects, such as its connection with technical activity, or began to explore new realms, such as that of life. The theory of evolution in particular has led to most interesting consequences. However, before discussing these points, we must first find our bearings in the history of the concepts "causality" and "finality."

Aristotle was the first to present a philosophical analysis of causality.[1] In his division he distinguished material, formal, efficient, and final causes. As we have seen in Chapter Three, Aristotle made this division, which is based on the working of a craftsman, universal by extending it to everything that comes to be, including the events of nature. For this reason he characterized all changes and motions as the actualization of a potency.[2] The "end" of a motion is not the point where the motion ceases for any reason whatsoever, but the "end" is the realized goal, that to which the motion was from its very start directed. The natural motions of the elements, such as the falling of "earth" and "water" and the rising of "air" and "fire," were considered the result of their tendency toward their "natural place," the place assigned to them in the cosmos.[3] Since the elements themselves were unable to know their goal, there had to be cosmic intelligences, responsible for the finality of the cosmos. When man produced things the final cause was the most important cause because it controlled all the other causes. Aristotle imposed this same hierarchy of causes on the natural order.

Medieval thought retained the world view of antiquity in which the central position was occupied by the final cause. Nevertheless, the center of emphasis shifted. Medieval man regarded the cosmos as a *created* order. Its Creator became the "First Cause," the Cause of all causes. The First Cause did not eliminate the other causes. The latter remained relatively autonomous, but owed their causality, whatever its nature, efficient or final, free or determined, to the First Cause to which they also owed their existence.

Given the intellectual climate of the Middle Ages, it was inevitable that in their reflection upon causality both philosophy and theology emphasized the causality of creation. The idea of creation permeated

---

[1]*Metaphysica*, Bk. V, Ch. 2.

[2]The strict definition of motion as motion is: "the actualization of the potency insofar as there still remains potency." While the motion is going on, the initial situation has been relinquished, the actualization has started but is not yet finished; hence there still remains potency.

[3]Cf. Chapter III, Sect. 2.

all their considerations of causality which thus came to be regarded primarily as *creative* causality, the production of something new.

Two main aspects characterized the change that occurred in seventeenth century thinking about causality. The final cause lost its priority through the new view of nature and, at the same time, emphasis shifted from the Creator's causality to a causality of nature functioning within the reach of explanations attainable by physical science. Unfortunately, the same terms continued to be used, which was bound to give rise to much confusion and misunderstanding.[4]

One such misunderstanding assumed that the efficient cause could now replace the final cause. This idea was true insofar as the final cause was now eliminated from the explanation of natural events and, under the name of finality, was considered of interest only for human activity and perhaps also for living nature.[5] It was not true, however, that the causality in which physical science retained interest could be equated with what the Aristotelians called "efficient cause." The Aristotelian efficient cause was too closely connected with the final cause to permit such an equation, if only because their efficient cause was primarily attuned to man as cause. But this reason does not tell the whole story.

If one insists on expressing the matter in Aristotelian terms, the causality considered by physical science should be called a "formal" rather than an "efficient" cause. True, this "formal" cause was one of a new type, for the formal cause spoken of by classical science— for instance, by Francis Bacon—was no longer the substantial form of concrete acting things, but became a functional relationship between *aspects* of things, laid down in a law. Physical science, it should be recalled, analyzes concrete things in their aspects and searches for relationships between these. In this way both the concrete things and their concrete activity are relegated to the background, for aspects or magnitudes do not act but merely are connected.

The fact that physical science continued, nonetheless, to speak of efficient causes must be attributed not only to the explicit intention of excluding final causes but also to the way physical laws were initially conceived, namely, as expressing the forms in which the

---

[4]For an excellent analysis of the change that occurred in the seventeenth century see H. Dolch, *Kausalität im Verständnis des Theologen und der Begründer neuzeitlicher Physik,* Freiburg i. Br., 1954.

[5]With respect to living nature the term "teleology" came into use.

natura naturans worked. The law itself was thus regarded as the expression of the efficient causality of nature. However, speaking of efficient causality became entirely meaningless when physical laws were no longer regarded as related to forms of nature but as related to forms of the knowing subject, for then there could no longer be question of expressing concrete activity in such laws. This shift to the subject occurred in the philosophy of the modern era.

Epistemological problematics, occasioned by classical physical science, exercised a strong influence on this shift, which modified causality from a relationship of real dependence into a subjective relationship of cognition. It should be kept in mind, of course, that, despite its empirical character, physical science remained provisionally a speculative science because its experimental nature did not clearly reveal itself at once. Physical science considered nature as it presented itself to the knowing subject. Thus the epistemological problem centered on such questions as, What guarantee does the knowing subject have that that which appears in his consciousness is reality?

The same problem permeated the philosophical approach to the question of causality. What guarantee do we have that the causal relationship in question does not exist solely in the subject's consciousness? For Hume there existed no such guarantee, and he therefore logically sought the core of the problem in the conditions which our impressions must fulfill if we are to speak of causality. When impressions regularly follow one another, Hume held, we interpret their succession as causality. Kant saw serious difficulties in Hume's ideas, particularly in the thesis that our causal interpretation is merely a matter of habit. Nevertheless, for Kant causality also remained a subjective category. There was, of course, opposition to these subjectivistic views of causality, and it would be misleading to think that causality was generally regarded as a subjective category. Nevertheless, the subjectivistic view dominated the discussion.

It is particularly interesting to note the way in which the problem was kept totally in the cognitive sphere, regardless of whether its solution was offered in an empiricist, rationalist, realistic, or idealistic sense. Significantly, the subject was nowhere mentioned as a *term* of the causal relationshp. (The subject was, of course, referred to as constituting the relationship.) As a result, free will as cause became nonsense. So-called free will was provisionally nothing but an unanalyzed case, a case too obscure to be discussed because it had not yet been sufficiently objectivized. For free will does not permit us to establish objectively observable successions, instances of conformity with a law. Only a very advanced analysis, patterned on physical science, some held, would make it possible to discover laws governing human activity and thus definitively eliminate free will.

Evidently, this narrowed the original broad range of meaning proper to causality. This narrowness was manifest in many ways. For one, the subject, as the creator of physical science, was no longer regarded as a cause. This restriction was possible only because the causal relationship had been fully objectivized into a relationship functioning within objectivity. And within this objectivity there was no room for creativity. The very purpose of causality was precisely to eliminate all creativity, any genuine newness. Thus it was possible to predict things. Everything that had happened, was happening, or was yet to happen was fixed in principle through conformity with categorical laws once a certain starting point was given.

Moreover, for an unprejudiced scientist it mattered little whether he thought about causality in idealistic or realistic, subjectivistic or objectivistic terms. Causality constituted for him the means *par excellence* to grasp reality as something essentially immutable and therefore, predictable. Consequently, the concrete working of nature attracted less attention, for it was regarded merely as the expression of constant laws. To the extent that the scientist worried about the creative aspect contained in the subject as the creator of physical science, he considered man's inherent forms of cognition necessary and always valid, so they, too, excluded all newness. The forms of cognition were supposed to be permanently established necessities of thinking.

Abstractly considered, there is no objection against an idea, which at first had a very broad range of meanings, being subsequently given a more precise and univocal meaning by the development of science. One may even say that such a process is entirely normal. The question, however, is whether a process valid for scientific concepts holds good for philosophical ideas also. Concerning the concept of matter, we saw how the fruitfulness of physical science is based precisely upon the plastic character of its methodic way of looking at material reality. Philosophy must safeguard this plasticity in its analyses lest it do violence to reality. But a concept of causality so narrowed down that entire regions of reality are disregarded cannot be fruitful. In reading Hume, it is very illuminating to see how often he uses the terms "cause" and "causality" in a much wider sense than the one he himself permits.[6] He could not dispense with this wider sense in trying to prove what he wanted to establish.

In a similar manner, the analysis of what occurs in physical science cannot dispense with the causal meaning of man as the *subject* of physical science. Accordingly, we spoke above about the narrowing of the concept "causality" and not of its being-rendered more precise. As long as man's share in physical science appeared restricted to being merely a *cognitive* subject, a pure consciousness, it might perhaps seem justified to eliminate this aspect of causality as belonging to an entirely different order. But this neglect was bound to have repercussions when the experimental character of physical science became manifest.

First of all, man as the subject of physical science, revealed himself not merely as a knowing subject but also an *acting* subject, and his active interference with nature could hardly be placed outside the realm to which causality applied. True, man's activity as such was nothing new, but hitherto it had seemed to be unimportant precisely within the sphere of science. Classical physical science had always proceeded in the light of the old idea of science; it regarded science as a typical concern of the mind to which the body and its activity hardly contributed anything.[7] Acting, handling things, assumed no role in the cognitive process and, equally important, had no function in the events of nature. With majestic sovereignty these events ran their course: man could look at them but was unable to interfere.

Secondly, as physical science developed into an experimental science, it became more evident how extensive man's interference in nature could go. This realization showed that man's causing, in the unity of his knowing and acting, could no longer be excluded from considerations of causality. For evidently the experimenter and the technician are efficient causes. The inclusion of man in causality, moreover, threw a new light upon the laws of nature, for these laws also are incorporated into man's activity and thereby receive a new meaning. No longer can they be regarded as resulting from a subjective way of knowing but share in the operational causality of man. They must express an aspect of reality because their acting in the realm of reality manifests itself most evidently.

---

[6] See *A Treatise on Human Nature*, Bk. I, Part III.
[7] Cf. Chapter I.

Clearly, the development of physical science has necessitated the rethinking of the whole problem of causality. And in our conviction this is of even greater importance than the critique of deterministic causality, which similarly has been provoked by a development in physical science, viz., quantum mechanics. This assertion is especially true because the discussion about the consequences of quantum mechanics frequently remains within the framework of the problems raised by classical philosophy. That discussion, then, continues to be limited to whether *knowledge* has an objective or a subjective character, whether the observer as *perceiving* subject has an essential influence or not—briefly, it argues about the validity of the principle of causality in the narrowed sense given this term by mechanistic determinism.

Thus the imposing question is whether the entire modern discussion of causality, which quantum mechanics raised—no matter how valuable it is in itself—is not unduly restricted to a narrow framework. For this discussion disregards both the operational aspect of physical science and the intimate connection between knowing and making existing in the contemporary technology to which science has given rise. For a revision of the idea of causality, the operational aspect of physical science is more important than the well known inadequacy of the deterministic connection revealed by the inadequacy of mechanical models.

2. THE MUTUAL RELATIONSHIP OF CAUSALITY AND FINALITY

Since it has become necessary to make room for human causality in physical science, finality has returned as an important category. Formerly, finality seemed to be of importance only for the activity of man, who was considered to have relatively few possibilities. Now, however, it appears that man can transform nature radically; therefore, man's causality, conceived both as efficient and final cause, must perhaps be regarded as the most powerful factor in the cosmos. This factor, however, is not like other factors, not a cause like the causes of nature. In a sharp analysis of Aristotle's theory of four causes Heidegger correctly points out that man, as efficient cause, is not so much a force working in nature as a discloser of nature's possibilities.[8] Considered merely as a physical factor, that is, merely as an

---

[8]"Die Frage nach der Technik," *Die Künste im technischen Zeitalter*, München, 1956, pp. 50 ff.

efficient cause, man is really unimportant in comparison with other factors. But in the unity of his intellectual knowledge and his handling of things, man makes the factors of nature serve him as instruments for his own purpose; precisely in this he is a great power in nature, a power which operates for its own purposes.

The distinctive character of man's causality compels us to revise the traditional interpretation by mechanism that causality, strictly speaking, never produces anything new but merely rearranges what is already given. It is true, of course, that an essential aspect of any causal explanation implies showing that what is new, what is to be explained, is only seemingly new.[9] But this "reduction of the new to the old" cannot entirely disregard what is new. The classical theory of causality could permit itself to ignore the new because it dealt only with nature considered as essentially static. Now, however, nature has shown itself precisely as dynamic.

It is not only the realization of human causality and finality as cosmic categories that makes it impossible to still regard nature as static. The theory of evolution in its own way does the same, for evolution also produces new forms in nature. Thus evolution, too, evokes the problem of causality as creative causality and, at the same time, that of finality; for as we will see presently, causality and finality are always interrelated.

It is hardly necessary to point out that the new view of nature, in which finality regains importance, does not mean a return to the old world view. In the old view final cause was external to nature, while in the new view man is involved as a principle of order present in nature itself. But even in this view, man can be conceived, of course, as a final cause external to nature insofar as man as a subject is not a thing of nature. For dualistically conceived, even in a moderate form of dualism, the spirit remains outside nature. However, according to the theory of evolution man himself has also come forth from nature. For this reason the theory of evolution compels us at least in our rethinking of finality not to limit ourselves to man's finality but to extend our reflection to the finality of nature.

However, even if provisionally we abstract from the theory of evolution, it would be impossible to ignore the finality of nature. For, if man as efficient cause is not so much a force acting in nature as a discloser of nature's possibilities, then clearly, in giving form

---

[9]Cf. E. Meyerson, *Identité et réalité,* Paris, 3rd ed., 1926, pp. 252 ff.

to nature, man depends very much on these possibilities. Expressed
in terms of finality, nature asks to be formed in certain ways; it is
oriented to certain forms, and therefore there is a final aspect in
nature. Admittedly, it is dangerous to speak in this fashion; the
terms can easily be misunderstood because of their historical connotations. Yet this danger should not prevent us from using them,
provided that the final aspect in question is not misinterpreted.[10]

The correct evaluation of finality cannot and should not disregard
the achievements of human thinking embodied in physical science
by Newton and Darwin, to name only two whose work constituted
turning points in man's way of looking at nature. In connection
with our problem here, one could perhaps say that their achievements warn us not to speak of the finality of the cosmos either as
external or as closed. For Newton showed that the order of nature
was an internal order, based on nature's conformity with laws, and
therefore not extrinsically imposed. Also he showed that these same
laws permitted an entirely different order from the one that actually
existed.

Darwin used fundamentally the same approach, but applied it to
the realm of the living in the perspective of an evolving world. The
accidental situation of the organism determined its adaptation by way
of natural selection. Remaining within the laws of nature as applicable
to living beings, evolution could have gone in entirely different directions than it actually took. If, then, there existed a kind of finality
in evolution, for instance, in being oriented to the origin of man, then
this finality must have been an *open* finality, a finality which essentially
includes chance. At the same time, of course, this finality must have
been such that it did not make a causal explanation powerless; that
is, like Newton, Darwin excluded a finality coming from without.
All this really means nothing more than that causality and finality
may never be divorced. Differently expressed, the type of causal relationship determines the type of final relationship, and vice versa.

From the preceding pages we know that there are many causal
relationships. The philosophy of the new era tried to clarify the concept of causality; but this attempted clarification was actually a
narrowing-down of causality, which was subsequently disclaimed by

---

[10]The term "finality" can perhaps be avoided, but not the problem to which
the term refers. O. A. Rabut, for example, speaks not of finality but of
instrumentality. This substitution of a different term, however, does not
eliminate the problem. Cf. Rabut, *Le problème de Dieu inscrit dans l'évolution,*
Paris, 1962, p. 65.

the development of physical science. We should be prepared to meet the same phenomenon with respect to finality. It may be necessary to emphasize this point, for among biologists there sometimes exists too much hope that a more exact and univocal meaning of the concept "finality" will make this concept useful for biology. Also new terms are often introduced, but there is no unanimity about them.[11]

More important than introducing new terms is realizing the broad range of meanings which such concepts as causality and finality can have. Within, and only within, that connected field of meanings the necessary distinctions and clarifications have to be made. The necessity of keeping in mind both the unity of the field of meanings and the distinctions that should be made in it becomes imperative when one takes the theory of evolution seriously. If matter, life, and spirit have the inner connection assumed by the theory of evolution, then it is inevitable that everything specifically proper to man must somehow be present in capacity both in living matter in general and in non-living matter. This statement does not mean that in man finality would be exactly the same as in things, but it does mean that whatever finality is found in man has something to do with the finality proper to things. In other words, not separations but distinctions are to be made, and these distinctions are absolutely indispensable.

3. The Various Meanings of Finality

The first and least disputed sense of finality is man's deliberate pursuit of a purpose. This kind of finality is present only in a knowing being that is aware of the goal as the goal and deliberately pursues this goal. The causality corresponding to this deliberate finality is free causality, that is, a causal acting which interferes in reality not by necessity of nature but as consciously intended by man.

A second type of finality can be connected with that first meaning. It is the finality encountered in higher animals insofar as they also reveal in their interplay of knowing and tending a kind of activity which resembles that of man. No matter, however, how far the similarity goes, there can be no question here of a genuine deliberate pursuit of a purpose since the animal has no self-consciousness and therefore does not know the purpose. Thus animal activity is not genuinely free activity. Nevertheless, because of the many differen-

---

[11]Cf., e.g., the survey given by T. A. Goudge, *The Ascent of Life,* London, 1961, pp. 191-205.

tiated aspects involved in animal activity, its action must be regarded as an incipient stage of free and purposive activity.[12]

The third sense of finality is also directly derived from the first, but in a manner entirely different from the second. The finality in question is present in machines and any type of mechanical contraption made by man. This finality is, of course, always of an externally imposed kind. The mechanism works for a purpose, but is not conscious of it. It realizes a purpose by virtue of the activity proper to the natural things which have been structurally united in the mechanism and therefore of necessity are attuned to the purpose.

In this connection the remark must be made that the machine may possess an *open* type of program, in the sense that its activity is co-determined by the registration of variable data. This is the case, for instance, with a thermostatically controlled system of heating. In such a case one can say that a kind of "power of perception" has been built into the mechanism. A mechanism may even possess a "memory" and a "capacity to learn." Nevertheless, no matter how ingeniously the mechanism has been constructed, it is evident that its programming and therefore also its finality have been imposed on it from without. This statement should not be misunderstood. That which the mechanism attains as its purpose never depends directly upon man's deliberate intention but is always determined directly by the way in which this intention has been embodied in the structure and programming of the mechanism.

Consequently, the purpose realized by the machine has a kind of autonomy.[13] Hence there is also question of an autonomous finality, in the sense that the machine is directed to a goal independently of the intention of its maker. This goal can be an embodiment of the intention of the maker, but it does not have to be so of necessity. In the order of causality, the structurally ordered natural causes proper to the parts of the machine correspond to the autonomous purpose in the above-described sense. Here again, therefore, we find that finality and causality are attuned to each other.

The finality exhibited by an organism is related to, but nonetheless clearly distinct from, that of a mechanism. The major difference is that the programming and structuring of a living organism are not

---

[12]Cf. Delfgaauw, *Geschiedenis en vooruitgang,* vol. 2, Baarn, 1962, Ch. III, Sect. 4.

[13]For the consequences of this autonomy with respect to the technical order in general, see the author's *Science and Technology,* Ch. XII, Sect. 2.

superimposed on it from without but present in it "by nature." Moreover, unless one wants to defend vitalism, he must admit that they are not present as a separate principle of life existing in the organism, but as flowing from the character itself of the material structure. For this reason the organism has a certain similarity to a mechanism, although the two remain different. This difference can be expressed in many ways. Remaining strictly on the level of physical science, in which the distinction between living and non-living manifests itself as a distinction in complexity, this difference may be said to consist in the fact that in the organism the macro-structures result from the micro-structures.[14]

If, however, interiority is also drawn into the picture, we must note that this interiority has something to do with the finality observed by physical science. From the perspective of interiority, finality manifests itself both as the tendency of the living being to self-preservation and self-development on the individual and specific level, and as the transcending of this level toward the development of the possibilities of life. This distinction especially gives rise to difficulties. As E. Mayr points out, it is not difficult for the biologist to accept finality in embryonic development and to speak even of *purpose,* because in this development it is clearly a matter of programming.[15] But the matter is different in the case of evolution, for here there is no question of programming and consequently no question of "purpose," i.e., finality. There is a great difference between these two cases, which we will consider more in detail later.

Provisionally we will remark that it would seem better not to speak of "purpose" in either case but rather of "finality." For even in the embryo's development there is no deliberate tending to something, as the term "purpose" would seem to imply. There is a distinct directedness, but this directedness results from the structured togetherness of the causal factors in a way similar to the case of a mechanism. The structural character is different, as we have seen above, but not the character of the individual material causal activities. And certainly, as in the case of a mechanism, the finality present in the organism does not *replace* any causal factor. If the physical and chemical factors in the embryonic development lead to results

---

[14]Cf. p. 62.
[15]Mayr, "Cause and Effect in Embryology," *Science,* vol. 134 (1961), pp. 1501-1506. For the programming governing the embryo's development, see C. P. Raven, "The Formalization of Finality," *Folia biotheoretica,* vol. V (1960), pp. 1-27.

which they do not attain outside the organism, then the reason does not lie in a superimposed finality but in the way the causal factors interact. The interplay of these factors has, of course, a special final aspect; but this special aspect also must be attributed to "something" in the causal factors, just as in the case of a mechanism. And this "something" itself also must be explained. Differently expressed, the causal explanation and the final explanation are different aspects of one and the same activity.

In all these cases of finality discussed above, we must say that despite their differences, there is relatively little dispute whether the term "finality" may be used with respect to them. The situation is different, however, with respect to the sense of finality in relation to inorganic nature. Obviously, in speaking about finality in inorganic things, one should not have in mind the kind of finality ascribed to them by the ancient world view, namely, an externally superimposed finality. If there can be question of finality in natural things, this finality must be internal. The development of physical science bears witness to this statement. But one can legitimately ask whether there is any sense at all in ascribing finality to natural things. To this question we think that an affirmative answer must be given. Our reasons are as follows.

As mentioned above, the final activity of man, machines and organisms is possible only if material activity itself has a certain directedness. For man's causing can reach its goal only when it can count on the way natural things work. This rule applies not only to the activities proper to man's own body but also to the extrinsic matter on which man acts. For example, because water always flows down, man can build hydroelectric plants. Because carburetted hydrogen mixed with air always burns and releases energy in the process, it makes sense to build a gasoline engine. Machines constructed by man are able to realize man's purposes only because the things of nature combined in these machines possess certain activities and these activities run their course in a certain way.

Also in man's own bodily activities, his intention must be realized in certain processes, which bring about this intention only by virtue of the fact that they run their course in a certain direction.

There is, as has been noted, always a distance between what man intends and the material realization of his intention. Precisely this distance points to the existence of autonomous directions in nature, which man must use to advantage. We use the terms "direction" or "directedness" here because they sound a little more neutral than finality. What is involved is not some mysterious kind of natural "purpose" in the strong sense of the term, but only the directions existing in nature, as they are expressed in the laws of nature. In other words, final directedness is not super-imposed upon causal actions as a guiding principle added to them from without, but the forces at work always operate in a determined way and by this very fact they have a certain directedness. This inherent directedness, then, is nothing but the determined way of operating proper to those causes, but now viewed, as it were, from the other side. For this reason it is sometimes said that the con-crete course of any motion in mechanics can be described both causally and finally.[16] Whatever description may be chosen, it refers to one and the same action.

Even in the case of a machine, one cannot really say that a final operation is superimposed on the causal operation. The operation of a machine has, of course, something special, viz., its specific struc-ture; but this structure is just as much concerned with the causal factors themselves as with their directedness. On the other hand, it is true that neither these causal factors nor their directedness suffice[17] to explain the origin of the machine. That explanation has to take into account man as the machine's efficient and final cause.

If we keep in mind that for the living organism it is equally true that its finality is based on the collocation of the causal factors in the organism's structure, then it is at the same time evident where the problem lies with respect to the causality and finality of evolu-tion. Unlike the machine, in the organism the structure has not been imposed from without. Hence the question is, How must the origin of this structure be explained? If physical science is able to provide an explanation, its reply will be found in none else than a reference to the original finality of inorganic things of nature. Their finality must contain more than the above-mentioned directions permitting an externally imposed organization; it must imply also an intrinsic tendency to a certain form of organization.

---

[16]Cf., e.g., Henri Margenau, *The Nature of Physical Reality,* New York, 1950, p. 423. According to Margenau, the causal description is made by means of differential equations, the final description by integral equations.

[17]They offer some kind of explanation, of course, because, in constructing the machine, man takes into account the causal factors involved and their directedness.

Here we find a new and rather imperative reason for not excluding the directedness present in nature from the general category of finality. Nevertheless, the large majority of biologists dislike the use of the term "finality" when it is a matter of explaining evolution. The term makes them think of a "metaphysical agency" which is supposed to control evolution, and such an agency is beyond the grasp of physical science. We must therefore examine whether the biologist's dislike of finality in reference to evolution is justified.

As we have pointed out in the preceding chapter, although in one respect there is a certain justification for the emphasis which the neo-Darwinists in particular place on chance in the process of evolution, in another respect this same emphasis obscures the real problem at stake in evolution. This problem is to see a beginning in the non-living that leads to simple living structures and to see in these simple structures the beginning of more complex and higher structures. The question of how this initial capacity developed, whether straight to the "goal" or along many accidental byways, is only of secondary importance. Paleontological materials give some indications pointing to a rectilinear development (orthogenesis), but according to most specialists this is merely appearance. Unfortunately, orthogenesis is often equated with finality, so that the rejection of finality really amounts only to a rejection of orthogenesis. Orthogenesis, however, is merely a certain form of finality and does not represent finality as such.

The finality to be concerned with in the explanation of evolution can be none other than the directedness of inorganic structures to form living structures. To discover and explain this directedness is the primary explanatory task of the biologist and the biochemist. This directedness does not lie beyond the grasp of physical science, and its discovery is the only possible explanation physical science can give in this matter. In principle, then, this task does not differ from that of the physicist who, on the basis of quantum mechanics, explains which atoms, in the chemical sense of the term, are possible. The physicist also tries to find the various kinds of "directedness" existing in the nucleus and electrons composing the atom and then calculates which structures are stable and which unstable.

True, the task of the biologist is much more complex because he deals with structures which, in addition to the complexity of inorganic matter, also possess the complexity of an organism. Nevertheless, in principle, his task is not different, at least not if one holds on to

Darwin's fundamental idea that it must be possible to explain evolution by means of physical science. The second question, then, is which of all the possible structures have been *de facto* realized and what was their line of descent. In the answer to this question chance plays a role.

Let us point out at once that chance is sometimes manipulated in rather strange ways. The opponents of Darwinism sometimes claim that the chance for an accidental origin of an organism or organ is exceedingly small—so small that it cannot be taken into account. Therefore, they add, something else must be at work here.[18] Chance alone cannot explain evolution. Depending upon the context in which this argument is placed, it is then followed by a vitalistic conclusion, a theistic conclusion or both. No matter, however, what the conclusion is, it does not at all follow from the premises.

First of all, let us remark that, according to the theory of probability, any combination, even the most unlikely one, can *de facto* occur.[19] Secondly, and this reason is more important, all such calculations are actually meaningless as long as we do not possess more exact knowledge about the inner directedness of atoms and molecules to form certain complex structures. Only when such knowledge becomes available, will it be possible to evaluate the true significance of the element of chance. At present we can merely say that the element of chance plays an important role in evolution, and nothing else. The fact that something else in addition to chance also plays a role remains, considered in itself, entirely within the explanatory framework of physical science; consequently, it points neither to vitalism nor to theism.[20]

These remarks are not at all meant to minimize the element of chance. On the contrary, chance must have played an important role, at least if we want to understand the special position of man in the

---

[18]See, e.g., Lecomte du Noüy, *Human Destiny,* New York, 1947, pp. 26 ff.

[19]One of the mistakes made in this matter is the following. One calculates, for example, how much chance there is that in a random distribution of cards each of four players will get thirteen cards of the same suit. This chance is exceedingly small and therefore need not be taken into account. This line of thought forgets, however, that the chance of obtaining the particular distribution which *de facto* occurs when the cards are divided at random over four players is, likewise, exceedingly small. Yet this chance is *de facto* realized.

[20]For an interesting but speculative attempt to base a law of tendency on the available data in evolution, see F. Meyer, *Problématique de l'évolution,* Paris, 1954.

cosmos. As Simpson expresses it, "His rise was neither insignificant nor inevitable."[21]

Such a statement, which is based on the element of chance, in the process of evolution, is diametrically opposed to the fundamental idea of Teilhard de Chardin, who regards the whole of evolution as directed to man from its very inception. Yet it is not very difficult to interpret both views in such a way that they are necessary complements of each other on the level which we are considering here, viz., that of physical science. We do not mean that the problem itself is a scientific problem, for in this interpretation we will have to take into account man as the pursuer of physical science. Religious backgrounds, however, which play an obvious role in Teilhard de Chardin and are not entirely absent from Simpson, need not enter into this interpretation.[22] The thesis of Teilhard that the whole of evolution was directed to man is entirely meaningful from the standpoint of physical science. The same, however, is true of Simpson's thesis.

Paradoxically expressed, an evolution directed toward man must include chance, so that the rise of man could also have not occurred. The paradox disappears as soon as we realize that man's place in the cosmos as its organizer is meaningful only if there is something to be put into order. If, as the ancient world view believed, the order of the cosmos did not include any element of chance, this order would come about in a fully autonomous way and would, therefore, exclude the possibility of being influenced by man. Precisely because the "random" arrangement of nature, which man finds, is not fully fixed by either an inner finality or an external finality (that of celestial spirits), many arrangements and transformations are possible. Man's creative causality can interfere in the constellations of natural factors because these constellations are governed by an "open" and not a "closed" finality. There are directions in nature, there is finality, since without directions man could not play with nature; but this finality is "open" in the sense that the various directions offer many possibilities.

Moreover, these same directions, left to themselves, make evolution along many different lines possible. In nature evolution is not

[21]*The Meaning of Evolution*, p. 144.
[22]We can also leave out of consideration the fact that Teilhard occasionally thinks in orthogenetic and vitalistic terms. It is regrettable that he does so, for neither one nor the other has a direct bearing on the true content of his thesis.

governed by a single all-encompassing cosmic finality; otherwise the rise of man would have been inevitable. But if man's rise had been inevitable, it would also have been entirely superfluous. For, what could possibly have been the function of man in a world that developed along an inevitable line?[23] For this reason we must say that, if evolution was directed toward man, it could only be an evolution which appears to us as evolving more or less "by chance" toward man.

One could object, of course, that Simpson's above-quoted statement is somewhat exaggerated even from the standpoint of physical science. For, if it is true that all matter contains a capacity for becoming man, then this capacity is bound to attain realization somewhere in the universe, even if the straight road to this realization is not prescribed. For the law of large numbers applies here also. These considerations, however, do not contradict the fact that within the framework of evolution on earth the rise of man must appear to us as not inevitable.

Finally, we must draw attention to another sense of finality, which is perhaps the sense most disputed and also most misunderstood by its defenders as well as its opponents. We mean finality in the sense of the finality of creation, as the intention of the First Cause. The reason why this sense is most disputed is not difficult to see. No sense of finality has been as much abused as this one; creation was pressed into service to fill all the gaps remaining in the lines of causality and of finality. As we have seen in the chapter on evolution, the history of the evolutionary theory reveals a constant abuse of the idea of creation. This misuse justified asking whether, with the progress of science, it would still be meaningful to speak of a Creator either in the order of causality or that of finality. Should we not expect that the remaining "gaps" in the causal and final explanations—these two are closely connected—will be filled in the future, and then all possible reasons for appealing to the Creator as the First Cause will have been eliminated?

We may begin by pointing out that the matter can also be seen differently. One could ask whether man's "belief" in the possibility of integral scientific explanations is not precisely a condition for a pure "belief" in creation. However, before we attempt to discuss

---

[23]One could reply that, as spirit, man could *contemplate* the cosmos. However, strange as it may seem, even this *contemplative* spiritual activity has shown itself to be dependent upon order-creating operational activity.

the answer to these questions, which go far beyond the present context of our discussion concerning finality, it will be desirable to make a few remarks about matters that do pertain to this context.

First of all, the discussions about finality are always characterized by much sensitiveness. Sometimes one has the impression that the necessity of a Creator stands or falls with the demonstration of finality or of no finality. This situation is rather strange, for, no matter how far the possibilities of explanation by physical science may extend, they should always stop before the fact that material reality exists.

Nevertheless, to a certain extent one can understand this strange attitude toward finality. So long as material reality does not seem to be more than simple "raw" nature, it does not seem to demand a Creator, at least not a Creator with the connotations attached to that term in Christian thought. Material reality itself is simply regarded as the anonymous primordial ground of everything that is, and this ground does not claim any special prerogatives. If, on the other hand, there are clearly final tendencies in material reality, then it no longer seems justifiable to take only matter into account, for finality would inevitably seem to point to an intelligent "purposer" behind material reality. For this reason it appeared most urgent to prove or disprove whether there exists in nature an order whose final aspects go clearly beyond the power of a material reality that is entirely disconnected from any bond with an intellect. This urgency also accounts for the emotional involvement surrounding the discussion of the role played by chance in the explanation of evolution. If chance plus the existing material reality could explain the entire order of life, man inclusive, then a Creator in the sense of a Christian God would be superfluous.

This context, in which the discussions about finality and chance ran their course, was bound to distort the problem of finality. The proponents of finality searched for a finality endowed with the characteristics able to render the services expected of it, and its opponents just as eagerly sought to strip finality of such characteristics. The most eloquent example of this distortion was the attempt to see in the process of evolution the guiding hand of the Creator, just as others had always recognized God's guiding hand in history. But how should one be able to see this guiding hand?

As we have pointed out above, an evolution which includes chance can be said to be directed toward man in a more meaningful way than an evolution which goes, as it were, straight toward man. Which of these two types of evolution would most eloquently point to God's guiding hand? This question cannot be answered on the basis of a mysterious pre-knowledge of God's way of working. The warning sounded by Descartes, one of the founders of the modern era, is still valid: What do we know about God's intentions? All we can do is study reality as it is given to us. For this reason a divine intention can be hidden behind an evolution running its course by chance, just as much as behind a more orthogenetic kind of evolution. Simpson, it seems, realized that when he wrote: "It [the mechanism of adaptation] turns out to be basically materialistic, with no sign of purpose as a working variable in life history, and with any possible Purposer pushed back to the incomprehensible position of First Cause."[24]

In all this, however, the crucial question is what possible sense it can still make to speak of a First Cause. Is matter with its fundamental properties not sufficient to explain the whole of evolution, even in its final directedness to man?

4. Creative Causality

As was pointed out above, the discussion about finality shows that for many there was hardly any difficulty in regarding matter as the origin of all reality, provided this reality did not have any final aspects. On the other hand, we noted, a more profound reflection on the idea of creation shows that this idea does not permit us to conclude to any particular type of finality. This final aspect, then, can conveniently be left aside in considering the idea of creation. What cannot be left out of consideration, of course, is the fact that somehow evolution has given rise to man. This fact throws a strange light on the ease with which some people accept matter as the source of all reality.

On the one hand, they represent material reality, and the causal aspects inherent in it, as very simple and thus hardly worth the trouble of explaining. Matter is there, and that is all there is to it. On the other hand, however, matter is made to bear the entire burden of explaining everything, including man himself as a knowing being. If it is really true that man can be explained by matter as an inner unfolding of the wealth of being that is in principle already present

---

[24]*The Meaning of Evolution,* p. 101.

in matter, then matter is not at all that simple "raw" stuff that "is there." The existence of matter is then full of mysterious depth, and its causality is then essentially a creative causality and not merely a causality that keeps things on the same level.

There is no escape from this dilemma. If one takes evolution seriously and especially the rise of man in evolution, then one cannot be satisfied with a concept of matter that is not endowed with great inner potencies, potencies which go far beyond the traditional content of matter. At once the entire mystery of being is then raised even with respect to matter. If, on the other hand, one does not regard the passage from non-living to living and from living to man as unfoldings of being but as additions to being, then the question arises: Where do the vital principle and the human soul come from? The author's standpoint in this matter is sufficiently clear from the preceding chapters; we merely mention it here to indicate that it is not easy to avoid the question of the First Cause, regardless of whether one thinks vitalistically or mechanistically. For this reason, as we have pointed out in Chapter Four, the problematics of creation is *sui generis;* it lies on another level than that of the explanatory possibilities proper to physical science or that on which the issues of the essential difference between living and non-living, living and man are raised.

The necessity of distinguishing these levels, however, does not mean that the problems in question are entirely unrelated. The contrary is true. While it does not matter much whether integral evolution is right insofar as the necessity of *raising* the problem of creation is concerned, the same cannot be affirmed with respect to the way in which this problem is subsequently envisioned. For the further development of the problem it is important to know whether the rise of man can be explained as an inner unfolding of matter or whether evolution must be conceived in a different way, viz., as an evolving toward man in such a way, however, that the rise of man himself is the result of a special creation which endows the body with a spirit.

As we have noted before, the thesis of man's special creation sounds rather vitalistic, but this alone is not sufficient to reject it *a priori.* The thesis could be rejected definitively only if man would succeed in recognizing himself in capacity in matter and would, at the same time, understand how this capacity could realize itself in a certain way. Undoubtedly, the attempt to do so is an extremely ambitious order, but is it *per se* impossible? At any rate, as we have pointed

out in the preceding chapter, an appeal to creation to make the rise
of man conceivable does not remove the necessity of trying to find an
explanation in terms of physical science because, as a causal explanation, creation is too general.

The problem at stake here, however, is a counterpart of the
preceding question. We must ask, Can an explanation in terms of
physical science itself ever be sufficient in the sense that it would
make the explanation through creation superfluous? Strictly speaking,
this question does not yet formulate the problem in an entirely
correct fashion. The first point to be raised is how would one eventually have to understand the relationship between the two explanations?
This is exceedingly difficult to answer since very little is known as
yet about the range of the explanatory possibilities of physical science.
Or might it at least be said that certain limits on both sides are
clearly established? For instance, is it certain that physical science
can never explain the "leaps" occurring in the theory of evolution
because such "leaps" simply cannot be explained in any other way
by an appeal to creation?

That claim is sometimes made. J. Hollak,[25] for example, writes:
"In my opinion, the nature of life as such shows with absolute certainty the impossibility of the evolutionary hypothesis which, with
respect to the three material levels of life, makes each lower grade
be the productive subject of the passage to a higher grade." The
three levels, he holds, are essentially irreducible. For this reason the
evolutionary tendency may exist on a certain level but it does not
transcend the limits of that level. Man, therefore, is "an *original*
beginning and not the product of an animal tendency to evolution."
Man is the being "which both is and accomplishes the transition as
such from animal being to human being. The animal tendency to
evolution is *not* immediately directed to being-man, man is *not* its
product, but man is, precisely as *man,* the *direct continuation* of the
animal tendency to evolution."[26] Hollak adds that "an idea of
evolution which refers the material cosmos directly to man (= evolutionism) cannot be brought into harmony with the idea of a *created*
cosmos."[27] He bases this statement on the consideration that the
grades of being have their mutual relationship only because they are

---

[25]"De wording van de menselijke geest," *Annalen v.h. Thymgenootschap,*
vol. 51 (1963), p. 120.
[26]*Ibid.,* p. 125.
[27]*Ibid.,* p. 121.

first separately united in a hierarchical order with the Infinite Being, the *Maxime Ens.*

Undoubtedly, as we have previously pointed out, the clear difference of level between the grades of being is a typical difficulty affecting all considerations of evolution. It is questionable, however, whether, given the present state of human knowledge, we are justified in judging the matter in so definitive a way as Hollak does. But let us abstract from this point and consider the topic of this section. Is it true that the acceptance of integral evolution of necessity demands the rejection of creation, and vice versa? We must confess that we do not see why. Why should a created cosmos not be able to be a *genetic* unity, in addition to being a hierarchic unity of being?

Hollak's idea that "the *'plus' itself* is the *passage* as *such* from the lower to the higher"[28] repeats the age-old principle, which we have discussed before, that a potency alone never realizes itself as a "plus" but always does so only by virtue of a "plus" that is already there. For Hollak, as for many others, this principle functions in a twofold way. Within the explanation of evolution it shows that the "leaps" must always be brought about by a subject which is already this "plus." But it functions also to show the necessity of creation since this new subject can be there only by virtue of the Creator. These two functions demand a detailed examination because they go to the heart of our problem.

The principle "Nothing is reduced from potency to act save by a being-in-act" is of Aristotelian origin. This alone is sufficient to make us suspicious of this principle if we keep in mind the world view in which it played a role. On the basis of this principle, moreover, Aristotle, followed by Thomas Aquinas, saw no difficulty in spontaneous generation, for the sun was a sufficient being-in-act. As a "spiritual" cause the sun was in a higher order than the living beings whose spontaneous generation had to be explained. The question, however, is whether the principle of causality involved here is still valid now that the Aristotelian world view has collapsed and man thinks differently about causality, especially because of the development of physical science. No matter how justified this question is, it is not answered simply by being raised. For, as we have seen, man must be extremely prudent in drawing conclusions regarding causality from the development of physical science. History reveals that the way causality was spoken of in classical physical

---

[28]*Ibid.*, p. 122.

science did not always agree with the way in which causality functioned in the same science.

It appears that physical science makes use of the above-mentioned principle of act and potency but in a much more refined way than did Aristotle. Aristotle's reference to the sun as the cause of spontaneous generation does not at all explain why eels arise precisely from *mud* and why only *eels* arise from it. The reference to the sun leaves all these possibilities open and really does not explain anything because it explains everything. But when modern physical science seeks an explanation for abiogenesis, it wants to discover in inorganic matter a capacity that can explain why certain organisms arise from it and, at the same time, to know how this capacity is actuated. In other words, it applies the same principle in a much more critical way. A less speculative example will illustrate this critical element. Aristotle had little trouble explaining the fact that an egg develops into a chicken; this also was a passage from potency to act and took place through the causal influence of the chicken that laid the egg. Yet, modern biology finds serious problems in embryonic development precisely because it inquires very concretely into both the capacity and its actualization.

These simple examples reveal something else. As more became known about matter and its own activities, the center of gravity in the application of the principle in question underwent a shift. For the ancients matter was largely passive, consequently they emphasized being-in-act as the explanatory cause. Now that more activities are ascribed to matter itself, so that its self-development becomes possible, the focal point of explanation has shifted to matter. In this way justice is done to an aspect that classical science originally placed in the foreground, namely, the idea of showing that the new is only seemingly new. At the same time, when biology and the theory of evolution apply causal considerations, they connect this classical aspect with the creative aspect proper to all causal events as such. Thus the possibilities of scientific explanation are enriched, but on the other hand, the limitations of this kind of explanation clearly reveal themselves, for precisely this creative aspect evokes problems.

Considering all this, the use of the principle of causality to prove the need for a special creation whenever matter is "raised" to the level of spirit is, we think, fundamentally a relic of the way in which this principle functioned in the old world view. This conclusion, however, does not mean that the principle itself is undermined either insofar as it functions in physical science or insofar as it plays a role in the problematics of creation.

To prevent confusion between the two ways in which the principle functions, we will try to approach the problem of creative causality in such a way that all danger of mistaking one for the other is excluded. The starting point of this attempt is twofold. First we will assume, as we have tried to substantiate in the preceding chapter, that in matter one may see the capacity for life and for spirit; secondly, we will assume that this capacity can be realized without appeal to any other causes than those which govern the complexification of the material structures and which, consequently, also govern the transition from non-living to living and from living to man. This second assumption remains provisionally a gratuitous hypothesis, but one which lies at the root of the evolutionary theory, because this theory holds that matter can be considered as the origin of all reality.

For an understanding of this entire line of thought it is essential to see that, even if we provisionally abstract from the problematics of creation, any consideration of matter as origin always remains a partial consideration, no matter how highly we regard the findings of physical science. For at most physical science can explain that the complexifications which occur are necessary complexifications. While levels of interiority appear to correspond to these complexifications, the true meaning of this interiority itself is understood only through man's self-experience. Differently expressed, that which man recognizes as a capacity for spiritual being he does not know, as such, on the basis of his knowledge of matter but recognizes on the basis of his self-knowledge. In other words, man himself is always presupposed in all knowledge of matter.

Accordingly, it will always remain necessary to consider man himself also as origin, even if the future would verify our assumption that physical science on its level can explain the origin of life and of man from matter, and thus fully justify its regarding matter as their origin. For even in that case it remains man who realizes that he has originated from matter, who recognizes himself in matter, by virtue of the transcendental openness given to him in his cognitive power. Any reflection upon matter as origin presupposes the presence of man, for only in man does there exist the possibility for matter to arrive at consciousness of its mode of being and of its potencies for development. In the order of time these two origins cannot be united, of course, but this points to the relative character proper to both origins. Man refers to matter, and matter refers to man, but neither can fully explain the other. The knowing man finds matter, he makes it transparent through his knowledge, but he does not create matter. On the contrary, he is dependent upon it. Matter, on the other hand, gives rise to man, but its "production" of man runs its course according to a pattern of development which matter itself neither knows nor creates, just as it does not create itself. Regarding matter, one cannot even say that it finds itself and its potencies. It is man who, finding himself, also finds at the same time matter.

These ideas are, of course, far ahead of the possibilities of explanation which physical science has at present. Science is still unable to see life presaged in the non-living, and the evolutionary explanation of man from inorganic matter still lies beyond the horizon. Nevertheless, it is useful to envision this possibility, not only with respect to the question of the view to be taken of man, but also to make us realize that the increasing range of possible scientific explanations does not at all remove the problem of creation. Let us add, however, that this increase forces us to formulate the problematics of creation in a more purified way because it makes this question all-encompassing and penetrating.

If it is meaningful to speak of a First Cause, then this cause must encompass both these origins in a timeless way. It is not sufficient to say that the First Cause stands at the beginning as the cause which make matter exist, so that matter can subsequently develop toward man, for the First Cause stands also at the end as origin of man. Because the Creator unites both origins in a timeless way, He is always present in all workings, in all development, and in all thinking about these matters.

Viewed from this standpoint, any appeal to the Creator as the special cause explaining this or that particular development appears to be a violation of both His transcendence and His immanence. In such an appeal the Creator ceases to be the timeless origin of everything, for He is considered necessary only on some occasions and not on others. For instance, He is not needed to explain the transition from protozoa to metazoa, but He is needed to explain the passage from animal to man.

In a very interesting study, which in many respects may be considered to be a paraphrase of the old principle that "nothing is reduced from potency to act except by a being-in-act," the philosopher

and theologian Karl Rahner concludes that the thesis of special creation must not be limited to man alone but applies wherever a being
produces another being.[29] A new being is produced when a man
comes to exist,[30] but not only in this case. When a being produces
another being, there occurs something which Rahner calls an "exceeding of self" (*Selbstüberbietung*). In our opinion, this distinction
between the exercise of a being's own activity and that in which this
activity produces a new being, no matter how meaningful the distinction may be in other respects, should not be characterized by
referring to the presence or absence of "exceeding the self," but
at most by degrees of this "exceeding." Our reasons are as follows.

Man's self-experience teaches us that our own activity, even when
it does not produce another being, is always an "exceeding of self."
The philosopher, the artist and the man of research experience this
strongly in their creative work. That which they create is their
own activity but, at the same time, something that runs its course in
them, for they did not create their own abilities but received them
as a gift.[31] What they experience most strongly is something every
man experiences, namely, the relativity of the "self" present in their
"self"-activity. Thus it is certainly meaningful to speak of "exceeding the self," but this "exceeding" is characteristic of *all* activity,
human and subhuman, i.e., it applies not only to the activity of beings
whose selfhood is evident but also to that of beings whose selfhood
is less striking or even barely discernible.

If, then, the "exceeding of self" applies universally to all activities
of all beings, it offers no ground for a distinction between activities
in which creative causality is present in a special way and others
in which it is not present in any special way. Creative causality is
either always present or never. It all depends on the way in which
one wants to interpret the limitation of self-activity. If emphasis is
placed on self-*activity*, then this activity itself already implies a creative aspect insofar as it produces something new. If, on the other
hand, *self*-activity is emphasized, then one must say of every *self*
that the activity proceeding from it essentially "exceeds" this self
but nonetheless in a mysterious way is present precisely in this self.

---

[29] P. Overhage and Karl Rahner, *Das Problem der Hominisation,* Freiburg i.
Br., 1961, pp. 74 ff.

[30] The thesis of man's special creation in the evolutionary process is simply
an application of the much more general thesis that every individual human
soul is created.

[31] This statement remains true even if man would arrive at greater understanding of his abilities. Cf. Chapter VIII.

For this reason it is meaningful to consider the creativity of all reality as a "creative evolution," in which it is of secondary importance whether or not there are "leaps."

On the other hand, this creative aspect requires a source which contains all phases potentially in itself.[32] Such a source is required, of course, also wherever a "leap" occurs because at such points the creative aspect, the "exceeding of self," is greatest. However, even then this creative aspect does not mean a special creation but merely a greater intensity of the ever-present creative aspect. Considered in this way, it almost seems to be merely a matter of words whether we want to speak of special creation in reference to those points of the evolutionary process in which the transcending creative aspect reveals itself most intensively. This statement could be made not only with respect to the rise of man in the process of evolution but also in reference to the origin of any new human being, for as an autonomous person the child is fully new with respect to its parents.

All this, however, does not imply that it is wholly meaningless to speak of special creation with regard to man. But this meaning can be none other than the fact that God's general creative causality finds an apex in the concrete origin of man, who as self-presence is a creature in a special way because his self-presence makes it possible for him to be appealed to by God. For this reason the idea of special creation must be said to refer to the immediate relationship of every concrete individual man to God. Even if one does not want to speak here of God, it remains true that man is the being in which the problem of being comes to consciousness—with everything implied in this, i.e., not only the beings found by the subject but also this subject himself for whom these beings are. And the problematics raised by this consciousness of being is interwoven with the encounter of one's fellow-man, the other, who in a radical way relativizes the subject's originality.[33]

From these considerations we may conclude that the problem of creation is not at all a specific problem of finality. Creation transcends all categories. Both the causality and the finality of the creative principle giving rise to created reality can be known only from the causality and finality of this created reality itself.

---

[32]See the careful analyses of O. A. Rabut, *Le problème de Dieu inscrit dans l'évolution*, Paris, 1962.

[33]Cf. the splendid study of this topic by E. Levinas, *Totalité et Infini;* to be published by Duquesne University Press.

CHAPTER EIGHT

HISTORY AS EVOLUTION

1. The Key Position of Physical Science

The discovery of evolution as a real event is not without importance for man's view of himself. Evolution is not just another item of information to be added to the innumerable collection discovered by man in the course of history, but touches him to the core. More than ever before man feels himself connected with the material reality from which he has come forth. He knows, moreover, that he takes part in an evolutionary process which, although it did not originate from him, is nonetheless dependent upon him for its further development. Of course, the idea of development did not arise after the theory of evolution had been formulated, but this theory extended to the prehuman stage of the cosmos something which man had already discovered in history, namely, the possibility of progress. As has been seen in Chapter One, this possibility was first of all discovered in physical science, so that this science occupies a key position in history. Pursuing certain ideas mentioned in Chapter One, we will reflect here upon that key position.

Most writers about the theory of evolution point out that, with the arrival of man in evolution, an entirely new element has entered the scene. His arrival made certain factors that hitherto had controlled evolution lose their importance, or even eliminated them entirely; but, on the other hand, it gave greater power to other factors.

Within the perspective of the neo-Darwinistic view, which predominates among biologists, the most essential difference in evolution before and after the rise of man must be sought, it seems, in the character of adaptation. Prehuman evolution was controlled by natural selection, through which the organism was adapted to its external environment, but man adapts his environment to himself.[1]

---

[1] As in many other cases, the distinction made here is not absolute, for a living being also actively adapts its environment to itself. However, as has been noted previously, this active adaptation is permeated with passivity. It is not a conscious activity that proceeds in a progressive fashion. It remains determined by the species.

Because of this new relationship, other "laws" apply to the cultural evolution of man himself; in addition the natural evolution of other forms of life gradually loses importance because man deliberately interferes with them as elements belonging to his environment.

For a correct view of man it is important to remember not only man's radical distinction from everything else but also his continuity with all material reality. In spite of his self-presence, his being a person, man remains nonetheless a biological individual. In man, the biological and the material are taken up again on a higher level. The possibilities of matter that begin to unfold themselves in living matter arrive at full bloom only in man. In this sense nothing of importance is eliminated, and it is only relatively true that the original factors of evolution lose their significance.

To clarify the seeming obscurity of these remarks, let us develop the point more in detail. In his book, *The Uniqueness of the Individual*,[2] P. B. Medawar asks himself the meaning of the fact that as a rule *every* human individual is genetically unique: "What is the meaning of this diversity, i.e., what intelligible function does it fulfil?" Although this is "not a question one can very well ask of human beings," Medewar thinks that a meaningful answer can be given with respect to lower organisms but not with respect to man. Inborn diversity, he points out, makes for versatility in evolution. If this diversity were absent, adaptive selection would have nothing to act on, and the species would be left without any evolutionary resource. Curiously enough, Medewar adds, the absence of this diversity would be less harmful to human beings than to any other animals, for men can change their environment instead of letting the environment change them. "So far from being one of his higher or nobler qualities, his individuality shows man nearer kin to mice and goldfish than to the angels; it is not his individuality but only his awareness of it that sets man apart."

Medewar's suggestion that man's technical ability, by which he adapts his environment to himself, has little to do with his genetic diversity is not entirely correct. No matter how much one appreciates the fact that a biologist does not want to explain all human activity in a purely biological manner, the denial that the genetic diversity of human individuals has any meaning for specifically human culture is based too much on a radical separation of spirit and matter. Medawar's mention of angels in the above-quoted lines appears to

---

[2]Pp. 185 ff.

point to such a radical separation. Yet technology can hardly be considered an angelic affair. And, in any case, man's technical culture requires above all a plurality of talents if this culture is to be developed to any degree. The very complexity of the technical order in which modern man lives shows very clearly how many diverse scientific attitudes of mind and practical skills are needed to keep this order running and especially to make it a truly *human* order. Even in the realm of pure science it is impossible for a single man to appropriate all the different attitudes of mind characterizing the various sciences. These sciences demand different ways of life and fundamentally different abilities. The experimenter must be able to "think" with his hands, the surgeon must have sensitive fingers, and the theorist the ability to sit still, just as much as all three need excellent "brainpower." Moreover, man's material condition implies that the qualities needed for one particular talent or activity often more or less exclude those needed for another gift.

Considering all this, it is justified, we think, to conclude that genetic diversity is just as indispensable for the technical and social development produced under the direction of man's spirit as it is for biological evolution.

While biological evolution, as it were, blindly gropes its way, human evolution goes its way deliberately, but continues to be based on the same foundation. We do not simply mean that man, as spirit-in-matter, remains dependent upon the properties of matter as a kind of instrument serving his plans. Undoubtedly, this dependence remains, but the foundation in question implies more than that. That which was first at work in matter and which thereafter continued in life was a general capacity for being, which only gradually found its full unfolding on the human level. Nothing is eliminated, everything remains present on the higher level, but because of this higher level new possibilities revealed themselves. Teilhard's writings especially are permeated with this idea. On the one hand, the rise of man with his power of reflection meant something essentially new, but on the other, "man only progresses by slowly elaborating from age to age the essence and the totality of a universe deposited within him."[3]

What man takes up consciously is not a task, created entirely "out of nothing," which he is compelled to accomplish by material means,

---

[3] Teilhard de Chardin, *The Phenomenon of Man*, Bk. 3, Ch. I, Sect. 1 C (Torchbook ed., p. 180).

but a task which continues in a new way something that had already started in the cosmos.

An interesting difficulty presents itself in this matter. If we take the idea of evolution seriously, it implies a creative unfolding of being, with respect to which the clearly distinct gradation of levels indicates that there exists in the various beings a tendency to transcend their own level. On the human plane this would mean that man, as directing his own evolution, also tends to transcend himself. Teilhard de Chardin also feels this difficulty when he asks whether man's future development would not leave his being-a-person behind as a finished phase. Yet the value of being-a-person is opposed to such an idea.[4]

This difficulty needs to be placed in the proper perspective. First of all, with respect to the subhuman levels, nothing of value in them is lost on the higher level. (Nothing which characterizes matter, vegetative life, or animal life is lost on the higher level, but everything is incorporated in a higher synthesis.) What, then, could be the meaning of an evolution that continues in man without any essential loss of human value? Anything that would mean a loss of selfhood, identity, personal being, briefly, any loss of interiority would always be a loss and never a gain. Such a loss, moreover, would be a denial of the main line of evolution, which manifests itself in an increasing interiority. Man's further evolution, therefore, can mean nothing but a more intimate interiority.

So far there are no difficulties. These arise only when one asks how man's interiority is supposed to become greater. In this question we touch one of the most urgent contemporary problems of culture, one in which the key position of physical science becomes a matter of doubt. Is it not obvious that modern man regards progress merely as an increase in his ability to control and dominate the material world? Rather than pointing to increasing interiority, man's growing control of material reality seems to point in the opposite direction, for this control is all too frequently accompanied by a loss of humanity, a loss of personal values. Since this problem has been examined in detail in a previous book,[5] we will not develop it here, but limit ourselves to a single aspect, viz., that of the key position occupied by physical science.

---

[4]*Ibid.*, Bk. IV, Ch. II, Sect. 1, (pp. 257 ff.).
[5]van Melsen, *Science and Technology*, Pittsburgh, 1961.

As has been repeatedly stressed, man's self-presence and freedom are very relative because man has no inner grip on his materiality and vitality. Although man is matter and life, his self-presence illuminates his essence only partially. For this reason there is always a duality of body and soul, of matter and spirit, of exteriority and interiority, or of whatever other contrasting terms one wishes to use. For the same reason there is also the duality of two ways of knowing, one which by way of the senses goes out to the observable world, and one in which man's reflection directs itself to self-experience. For the same reason also there is the duality of activity, one kind referring to the "external world" and the other to man's self-perfection.

These dualities, however, should not be misunderstood. There is no real separation of body and soul; hence there is likewise no sense knowledge in which reflection is not present in an incipient way, just as there is no reflection which goes directly to the subject without the intermediary of knowledge running its course through the sense organ. The last part of this assertion is confirmed by the fact that all concepts in which self-reflection finds expression are analogous concepts, initially borrowed from the observable world. Likewise, there exists no activity that is solely directed to the "external world" nor an activity that is purely internal. Nevertheless, the duality exists and makes itself constantly felt.

According to this line of thought, a genuine evolution of man would be one which went toward an elimination of this duality, that is, toward an intensification of man's self-presence and freedom. But, we must ask, is such an evolution conceivable?

Everything, so it seems, indicates that the dual situation must be considered a fundamental situation of man as a spirit-in-matter, a situation that cannot be changed at all since it characterizes precisely man's level of being. In that case all human culture must remain within the possibilities offered by this fundamental situation, just as man's individual life remains within another dimension of this fundamental situation, the dimension of birth and death. For birth and death express in a most radical fashion man's defective way of being with himself. Through birth he begins to be, and through death he ceases to be.

Nevertheless, we must ask whether this fundamental situation is characteristic of man as such or merely of the present stage in the total process of evolution. On closer inspection this question divides itself into two. The first, which is the most radical, asks whether a passage is possible to a higher level of being than man's present level, to a level on which these dualities would be eliminated or at least greatly diminished. The second question limits itself to modalities within man's fundamental situation itself. It asks whether or not what we at present regard as an immediate consequence of the fundamental situation is really such a consequence. To each of these questions one must apply perhaps even more emphatically Medawar's remark that it is "not a question one can very well ask of human beings." However, it is characteristic of man that he does ask this kind of question, that he can place himself in his thinking outside his concrete situation, and that, strictly speaking, he always does that when he thinks. For all thinking contains an aspect of absoluteness which transcends all limitation and therefore also every situation, even though it remains true that every question is always asked from a situation.

In other words, these questions exist and are at least just as typical of man as any limiting situation. Man cannot give up attempting to answer these questions. For what else is his restless striving for knowledge, his ceaseless exploration of his own possibilities, but an attempt to answer the questions? It should be evident that in these attempts the second, less radical, question is more fruitful than the first because *de facto* the latter can be approached only by way of the first. If somehow, in a still unknown way, a passage is possible to an existence in which the person is more a person because he is liberated from his limiting duality, then the condition for attaining this passage must lie in the development of the possibilities existing on the level of man's present situation. But in what direction are these possibilities to be sought? Concerning the answer to this question the West especially has lapsed into a crisis situation due to the rise of physical science and technology.

Before the rise of physical science, the Christian West possessed a clear answer to both questions, although it did not consider the problems these questions raised in the perspective of evolution. Christianity distinguished life on earth, as man knew it—a life of extremely restricted possibilities—from man's future glory, a state in which man, taken up by God into His eternity, would live a life liberated from all material limitations and of all duality. Strange as it may seem, Christian thought about eternal life always retained a certain ambivalence with respect to the body's participation in this eternal life, and this ambivalence was connected with a similar ambivalence in the view taken of man.

When dualism prevailed, death meant primarily the liberation of the soul from the restricting bonds of the body. Life after death was seen as a purely spiritual existence, the type of existence which naturally belonged to the soul as a spiritual being. The special feature of this life after death was that the soul's continued existence would be a being with God, which would make the soul perfectly happy because it would contemplate the source of all goodness, truth and beauty.

By contrast, a less dualistic conception of man's possible survival after death centered its attention on a different point. A more eschatological interpretation played an important role here. This eschatological view spoke of the total destruction of the earth and the cosmos at the end of time, at least with respect to their present structures; but it also stressed a new creation in which man as man, that is, with body and soul, would live forever before God because the new earth would be taken up into God's glory. Here, then, the emphasis did not so much fall upon the soul's survival after death as upon man's resurrection, with body and soul, from the grave. This body, however, would not be man's ordinary body, rebellious against the spirit, but a perfectly spiritualized body.

All kinds of intermediary views were possible, of course, such as that which connected the survival of the soul with the resurrection of the body and regarded the soul, after its entrance into eternity, as awaiting the "last day," when it would be reunited with the body.

Regardless of what view was held, however, life on earth was considered meaningful only as the gateway to eternity. Within the temporal framework of his earthly life, man's eternal life was decided for good or for evil but not on the basis of earthly norms of success or failure but on the ground of man's internal disposition, his love for God. According to Christian conviction, however, man's love for God had to manifest itself concretely in his loving concern for his fellow-man, especially when the latter was suffering and in need. This point is of capital importance here. In his suffering fellow-man, the Christian encountered Christ Himself: "I was hungry and you gave me to eat; I was thirsty and you gave me to drink; I was a stranger and you took me in; naked and you covered me; sick and you visited me; I was in prison and you came to me" (Matthew 25: 35-36).

No matter what one may think about Christianity in its historical form, it certainly does not merit the reproach that it disregarded these words of Christ. Throughout history Christianity has always shown special concern for man in need. But this concern was always, especially in the past, viewed primarily in a supra-earthly perspective. Certainly, the Church's impressive concern for man in need was not inspired by the idea that this concern could ultimately develop into an effective struggle to eliminate man's need. And this idea, of course, could hardly have existed as long as physical science had not yet begun its role in disclosing the earthly possibilities open to man. The traditional Christian view of charity was unavoidably permeated with the old world view. Understandably, the collapse of this world view was bound to cause a serious crisis. And in this atmosphere of crisis, all the trusted old ideas had to be re-evaluated.

In its critical examination of the new possibilities offered for man's earthly life, Christianity was just as unfortunate as in its evaluation of the biological theory of evolution. Just as the evolutionary theory seemed to contradict creation, so the new vision of earthly reality seemed to conflict with the Christian ideas of redemption and of the future. The parallel should be clear. Although in the problem of the evolutionary theory and creation the question of man's origin stood in the foreground, while in the view of earthly reality man's ultimate destiny occupied the center, the crux of the problem was the same: the origin and destiny of man seemed to be moved from heaven to earth, from the realm of the unimaginable to that of observable reality. At least, that was the interpretation taken both by believing Christians and by those who saw in the new developments a reason to give up Christian faith as antiquated. Actually, however, the whole view was based on an insufficient analysis of the many problems that were mixed up and intertwined in the issue. As we have seen in discussing the theory of evolution, no matter how much this theory raises the question of man's origin, it does not eliminate the problematics of creation. Even if the evolutionary theory is right, the problem of creation remains. The same applies to the new view of the future and the problem of man's destiny. Let us develop this point a little more in detail.

No one can seriously claim that science's possibilities not only to assist man better in his need but also to eliminate this need effectively, in any way contradict the idea of Christian charity in its supra-earthly perspective. If those possibilities *seem* to contradict this idea, the only reason is that hitherto man's view of Christian charity has been *de facto* too closely associated with the classical view of the earthly possibilities open to man. Within the context of the old world view there seemed to be, indeed, but little room for such possibilities. Likewise, one cannot claim that the immediate motive of Christian charity, profound respect for each human being, no longer has any value. On the contrary, if the modern technical order needs anything at all, it is precisely this respect. Finally, one cannot claim that, because man has a task to accomplish on earth, he no longer feels the need of lifting a corner of the veil that covers the mystery of being and therefore also man's ultimate meaning and destiny.

Like matter, man himself as origin is unable to claim absoluteness. While at a given moment it may have become clear to him that his earthly activity has an intraworldly meaning, this meaning continues to demand a more profound foundation. Although, as we will see more in detail, man's earthly activity is perhaps able to make life more human, it possesses too much the character of a means to be itself the sole bearer of man's meaning. For this reason Christianity is certainly not antiquated by the sole fact that human existence can now also receive a new and earthly meaning, although it remains true that this new giving of meaning compels the believer to a profound rethinking of Christianity[6] and especially of its dogmas, if not in content, then at least with respect to their status.

Christian dogmas have too often been handled in the past as if they were revealed scientific theses, which could be opposed to other scientific theses discovered by man's own research. A sign of this way of handling dogmas may be seen in the still largely accepted theological view that theology constitutes a negative norm with respect to physical science.[7] This standpoint is rather strange if one recalls that in many cases physical science has acted as a negative norm for theology while not a single example is known in which theology has acted as a negative norm for physical science, unless, of course, one accepts as examples the cases in which physical science went very clearly beyond the boundaries of its competence. These transgressions, however, can be recognized as such by the internal critique of physical science itself because the method of this science is fixed. For theology, an internal critique appears to be less easy, which is perhaps connected with its rather unique

---

[6]For a detailed discussion of the problems connected with this point, see Albert Dondeyne, *Faith and the World*, 2nd impr., Pittsburgh, 1965.

[7]Cf. P. Overhage and K. Rahner, *Das Problem der Hominisation*, p. 20.

position as a science in the Middle Ages and with the less clearly established character of its method.

Anyhow, Christian dogmas can never be theses limiting the speculative freedom of the man of research, but are liberating truths, which belong to another level than that of man's scientific interests. Dogmas give the believer certainty; but this certainty leaves untouched all the uncertainties of the world, which continue to belong to the realm of scientific inquiry. If in former times dogmas seem to be more than we have admitted above, it is because there was then an insufficient understanding of Christian revelation itself. This revelation was understood in the perspective of the then current view of the world and of man and in connection with the questions evoked by that view.[8]

The crisis situation in which European culture has fallen finds a large part of its explanation in the fact that the Church had fixed herself too much in the pre-modern world as in a permanent "dwelling place." This dwelling in the past should not be understood so much in a material sense—though that too is perhaps true—as in a spiritual sense. It was that world with its scientific and technical possibilities, its cultural ideals, its customs and practices, with which the Church was familar. That was the world which the Church wanted to christianize and to which she had attuned her message and her institutions. The fact that the process of christianization encountered great difficulties did not unduly disturb the Church, inasmuch as she thought that she knew the reason, viz., man's sinfulness, the result of original sin.

In a certain sense, therefore, Christianity had learned to take the world for what it seemed to be. If the world did not want to listen to her saving message, the Church could not be blamed. The only thing that could make the world and its misery bearable was the idea that they would pass away. Thus the Church regarded everything *sub specie aeternitatis,* under the aspect of eternity, and she expected her faithful to assume the same attitude. In this perspective one can also understand why the Church assumed leadership, or at least patronage, in almost every realm of life. Science and art, no less than care of the sick and the weak, were above all means to serve man's supraworldly destiny.

---

[8]Cf. van Melsen, *Science and Christianity,* to be published by Duquesne University Press.

Meanwhile, to quote Huxley's expression, the world had begun to regard itself *sub specie evolutionis,* under the aspect of evolution.[9] Man believed in a better world, to be reached by his own efforts. The world no longer believed in a lost paradise but in a paradise to come. The Church eyed this "world in evolution" with suspicion, seeing such a belief as a mere continuation of man's original sin, his pride, which made him seek in man for what could not be found in him. The "world in evolution," on the other side, thought that the Church sought happiness where it could not be found, in a non-existing heaven.

The arguments surrounding the battle between the two visions of the future parallel those circling the biological problem of evolution. Just as the theory of evolution was attacked with theological arguments and theology with biological considerations, so also history was pressed into the service of the two opposing visions of the future. Christianity pointed to the destructive forces which since the rise of man's belief in progress had torn the world to pieces, and its opponents stressed how little Christianity had accomplished in the two thousand years of its history.

Such arguments generally lack the power of convincing, since the period of history about which man is well informed is much too short. It is as if one wanted to reject biological evolution on the ground that in the past few thousand years no new species have arisen. Thinking about the future must remain speculative for the simple reason that we cannot survey the future. Nevertheless, certain facts must be mentioned "under the aspect of evolution" because they make us pause and reflect. They are the following.

In the biological theory of evolution we are confronted with certain "leaps" to a constantly higher level of being. The most striking examples of such leaps are abiogenesis and anthropogenesis. In human history there are likewise certain "leaps" to a higher level. True, these leaps did not raise man to a level transcending that of man; nevertheless, within the framework of human existence they constituted important break-through points toward a richer form of being-man. In Chapter One we gave examples of such points in the rise of philosophy and the birth of physical science. Others could be added,[10] but in the more recent known history of mankind these

---

[9]J. Huxley, *Evolution in Action,* New York, 1957, p. 118.
[10]Concerning this matter, see what Karl Jaspers calls *"die Achsenzeit"* in Chapter One of his book, *Ursprung und Ziel der Geschichte,* Frankfurt, 1955.

two are undoubtedly the most important. The question which we have to examine now is what man's next break-through must be if he is to make another "leap" toward a new level of being-man.

We may begin by pointing out that, with respect to this question, it is meaningful only to speak of that which lies within the reach of man as we know him, for it is from this reach that the "leap" must be made. At the same time, it must be something that does not violate man in his being-a-person but makes him be more a person. But man will be more a person only when he grows in his selfhood, his freedom. In the present situation, however, man's selfhood and freedom are still far from perfect because, as we have seen, man's understanding of his materiality and his vitality are still very defective and therefore permit him only a very imperfect control over himself as a material and living being. Moreover, new possibilities for man's understanding and controlling of his materiality and vitality will arise only if physical science succeeds in penetrating more profoundly into the mysterious interconnection of matter, life, and spirit. Thus, understanding the possibility of evolution from matter to man becomes a condition for further evolution.

The understanding of this possibility is nothing but the central problem of biology itself and even of all physical science. For the ability of producing living, knowing, and self-conscious beings is the inmost possibility of nature, in which, using the terminology of our previous discussion, nature's macrostructure harmoniously corresponds to its microstructure. Hence the understanding of this correspondence is the central task of physical science. As long as physical science has not succeeded in this central task, it has not yet reached its fundamental aim. What is needed here is an "inner" break-through, a term which seems appropriate to indicate a break-through by which physical science would succeed, be it in a limited way, in understanding the interconnection of matter, life, and spirit.[11]

Undoubtedly, it is important for physical science to produce all kinds of technical structures as possibilities whose secret nature is forcefully revealed to the penetrating gaze of science. But it is much more important to understand how nature itself has realized its possibilities, for the simple reason that man himself is one of these possibilities. For, no matter how much technical achievements transcend in some respects the possibilities realized by nature itself,

---

[11]Concerning this limited way of understanding by means of so-called correspondences, see pp. 103 f.

these technical accomplishments are based upon man as their origin. Therefore, understanding how nature has produced man is more important than all technical achievements.

Let us emphasize again that in this understanding of man, we can abstract from the controversy whether anthropogenesis should be regarded as the infusion of a spirit or the becoming-spiritual of matter. In either case it is precisely the possibility of the event that has to be explained. This explanation, moreover, is probably a condition for any further progress with respect to the controversy in question. Pursuing this line of thought, one arrives inevitably at the conclusion that, with respect to the next break-through which man will have to make in his own human development, the key position will again be occupied by physical science. This conclusion gains in persuasiveness when one analyzes the argument that seems to contradict it most strongly, viz., the argument that the human sciences and the *Geisteswissenschaften* obviously must have a priority over mere physical science with respect to the development of man as man.

2. The Position of the Human Sciences

If the increase in man's self-understanding is important for mankind's development, one would at first be inclined to expect more help from the human sciences than from physical science. Since the physical sciences abstract from the specifically human aspects of man, how could they be of primordial importance for the development of these aspects? Where man as man is at stake, only the human sciences can provide guidance. Although they would have to take into account the aid that physical science can offer, they would proceed according to their own specific methods, attuned to their object, which is man himself. Any science which does not take the specific character of this object into account in its methods could only present a caricature of man. Thus, it would seem that the human sciences, and not physical science, are of primordial importance here.

Using the terminology of Chapter Two, one could even say that just as physical science owes its strength to the implicit vision of the object that is embodied in its method, so also the human sciences can be successful only if their method is based on a correct vision of man. No matter how one wants to express the specifically human aspect of man, it is certain at least that man is not simply and merely a part of nature, a thing among things, to be manipulated like any other thing. Man is above all self-existent, self-present and free, so that only a science which from the very beginning takes man's human character into account can say something about man that goes to the core of his being. While it may be true that the term "human sciences" deserves preference over the term *"Geisteswissenschaften,"* "sciences of the human spirit," because a dualistic conception of man makes itself felt in the latter, this change in terminology does not mean that the specifically human aspect expressed by the old term should be given up.

One can agree with all this and, nonetheless, retain the view that the above-mentioned break-through in physical science remains of fundamental importance for the human sciences. For, unlike physical science, the human sciences have no unanimity about the method to be followed. True, even in physical science there is much disagreement concerning the philosophical explicitation of the method of this science, but this disagreement does not affect the method it *de facto* follows. The method is firmly anchored in physical science; but in the human sciences the controversy affects precisely the method that is to be followed. Philosophical controversy is mirrored in the actual pursuit of the human sciences, it manifests itself in the way in which problems are raised and their solutions are proposed.[12]

Almost inevitably the question arises whether this situation does not result from a possible lack of maturity in the human sciences. Does not every science have to pass through such a stage before it becomes mature? The history of physical science itself shows that this question is meaningful, for this science also went through an initial phase in which its method was the object of controversy. The seventeenth century empiricist or rationalistic interpretation of the method proper to physical science was not merely concerned with the *philosophical* interpretation of this method, but with the very method itself. Descartes attached little importance to the experiment, and the modern sociologist or psychologist will certainly understand his complaint that there existed no uniform and objective method for expressing experimental results. Meanwhile this method has been discovered in the instrumental registration of physical science.

In biology the methodological struggle has lasted longer than in physics or chemistry, as is evidenced by the controversy between

---

[12]See, e.g., J. Rex, *Key Problems of Sociological Theory*, London, 1961; S. Strasser, *Phenomenology and the Human Sciences*, Pittsburgh, 1963; E. Nagel, *The Structure of Science*, London, 1961, chaps. 13 and 14.

mechanism and vitalism. But here also the issue has been decided, at least with respect to the aspects of biology that belong to physical science. The matter is still unsettled with respect to animal psychology and animal sociology, but this remaining controversy is an extension of the methodological struggle of the human sciences rather than that of physical science.

It would be superficial, however, to ascribe the human sciences' failure to arrive at a unanimous method solely to the fact that these sciences happen to be younger than physical science. In the seventeenth century the nascent physical science did not even have an example to follow, since this science was the first positive empirical science. Physical science could not even find a precursor in astronomy, which had reached considerable development even in antiquity, for with respect to method astronomy continued to be regarded as a mathematical rather than a physical science far into the Middle Ages. Anyhow, were there nothing special involved in the distinction between physical science and human science, one should expect that the more recent science would not have much trouble in following the example set by the older science, especially when one considers that Auguste Comte, the founder of human science as a positive science, did not fail to point to that example. Moreover, Comte's suggestion was followed in the nineteenth century. In fact, this is evident from such expressions as *Geisteswissenschaft* and *geisteswissenschaftliche* method, which were coined precisely in protest against the allegedly exaggerated dependence of nineteenth century human science on physical science.

Accordingly, although we may not ascribe the continued controversy about method solely to the human sciences' youthfulness in terms of years, it appears to have something to do with their inner lack of maturity. They still lack a firm methodic grip on their object. For as soon as a method is actually successful, discussion about it ceases, at least among those who pursue the science in question. If, next, we ask the reason why the method of the human sciences has not yet managed to obtain a solid grip on their object, a relatively simple answer suggests itself: the object of these sciences is exceedingly complex. Put in this somewhat vague form, the answer will probably be acceptable to opponents as well as defenders of the physical method in the human sciences; but they will interpret the answer differently. The defenders will say that man, considered as a scientific object, is so complex that, as long as biology has not succeeded in explaining life, one can hardly expect the human sciences to explain man. The opponents of the physical method will say that man is complex because he belongs to several levels which constantly compenetrate one another. Man is matter but spiritualized matter. He is freedom but this freedom is conditioned by matter. He is determined but at the same time able to know his determinisms and make them serve his purposes. In other words, there is not simply question of complexity on a single level but of complexity resulting from the interplay of many levels.

Inevitably the dispute over the method of the human sciences brings to mind the old controversy between mechanism and vitalism. Recalling this controversy will be fruitful if the distinctions we made in discussing it are also kept in mind. For example, one can be convinced that man has a special and unique status of being and, at the same time, think that man, considered as an object of science, can be studied only by methods similar to those of physical science. Or, as a more prudent formula expresses it, man can be studied fruitfully at least also by such methods. If such possibilities exist they must be exploited.[13] Just as a proponent of mechanism in biology does not necessarily have to be a materialist in the philosophical sense, so likewise not every defender of the physical method in the human sciences has to deny the special character of man.

It has not been our intention to discuss the controversy about method in the human sciences here in an extensive way. This would not be needed, anyhow, as soon as it is evident that this controversy is essentially connected with man's inability to have a clear insight into his own relationship with his materiality. One could perhaps even offer the following dilemma. Regardless of who are right—the proponents of the physical method in the human sciences or those who require a special method—in both cases an "inner" breakthrough of physical science is needed to make progress. With respect to the defenders of the physical method there is no need to argue the point since they are already convinced. For the proponents of a special method in the human sciences the conclusion still follows of necessity, but less directly, in the following way.

According to the viewpoint requiring a special method in the human sciences, it remains necessary that these empirical sciences start with a correct view of human existence.[14] We grant that at

---

[13]Cf. D. Krech, *Brain Chemistry and Adaptive Behavior,* Nijmegen, 1963, p. 13.
[14]Cf. S. Strasser, *Phenomenology and the Human Sciences,* p. 312.

once, but what is necessary need not be sufficient. The essential point in the empirical human sciences is to have a correct understanding of the way in which the activity of the spirit is embodied in materiality. Without that insight, precisely that condition is lacking which must be fulfilled if the empirical human sciences are to be more than purely descriptive sciences. But that insight requires knowledge, gathered by way of physical science, of the way in which material structures condition the activities of the spirit.

Moreover, in addition to this direct aid to the human sciences, it is perhaps also possible that physical science has crucial importance for the acquisition of a philosophical insight into human existence that can be fruitful for the specific method of the human sciences. However, the importance which the break-through in physical science can have for philosophy is a matter that will be discussed in the next chapter.

Summarizing, we do not want to conclude that a break-through in the human sciences is not of very great importance or that the method of the human sciences will not be essentially different from that of physical science, but only that the break-through in the human sciences will inevitably have to wait for the break-through in physical science.

This conclusion should not be misunderstood, of course. It certainly does not imply that until then we would have to stop the pursuit of the human sciences. First of all, we never know *a priori* whether data acquired by the human sciences may not be needed precisely to make the "inner" break-through of physical science possible. For we should never forget that understanding material and vital functions in relation to specifically human activities presupposes an understanding of these activities, especially in their empirical aspects. It can hardly be doubted that our knowledge will have to be acquired by means of the above-mentioned correspondences. On the one hand, these correspondences will be between things that have been investigated by physical science, in which the aspect of registering observation will be predominant and, on the other, specifically human activities which, no matter how much they need to be observed in empirical inquiry, will always be understood also in terms of the observer's inner involvement in them if he is to grasp their human meaning. To illustrate the matter with a concrete example, regardlless of how profoundly a psychiatrist is convinced that all mental illnesses are essentially based on organic deviations, he will make no progress whatsoever unless he carefully describes and interprets the mental "deviations" as *human* disturbances.

This example leads us to the second point, which likewise throws light on the proper and irreplaceable value of the special method pertaining to the human sciences. No matter how convinced one is that the possible cure for "mental diseases" must ultimately be found in understanding the defects in organic structures, this conviction does not relieve medical science from its duty to help, to the best of its ability, the living human being with defective humanity to be as human as it is possible for him to become. This duty is not merely a provisional emergency measure. The insights acquired in helping someone whose freedom is affected will always remain valuable because human beings will always have to help one another to realize their freedom for themselves. This brings us to the third point, which is the most important for an adequate understanding of the contribution which physical science can make.

If the "inner" break-through in the physical sciences would make it really possible for man to gain an insight into his own natural determinisms on their various levels, this success could mean a genuine growth in humanity, a more intense spiritualization of the body. Of course, the success would not mean an *automatic* increase in man's humanity, for an increase in humanity is an increase in freedom and an automatic increase of freedom is a contradiction in terms. Only the possibilities for human freedom can be increased, while man himself must attempt to realize these possibilities. The aim of the "inner" break-through in physical science should never be to manipulate man and to make a mockery of his freedom. The idea, therefore, is not, as is sometimes claimed, that a better understanding of the bodily conditions underlying man's behavior will make it possible to influence this behavior in the desired social direction much more effectively than can be done at present. True, this possibility may perhaps be implied, but it should not act as a norm for the evaluation of the issue.

An example may clarify the point. A man who suffers from a cerebral tumor is deprived of the possibility to lead a human and free life. By removing the tumor, a surgeon can restore the person's freedom. This case refers to a pathological condition, a deviation from the human norm. There is no particular problem regarding this norm. Everyone considers it ab-normal if there is a tumor in the brain which affects the mental powers of a patient whose history before the tumor revealed the presence of those mental powers. We are happy that the surgeon's activity is able to restore the normal order. However, what norm do we accept when we find it normal that relatively few people are able to pursue university studies or perform creative work?

This norm appears to be no other than the "raw" norm of the *natural* distribution of talents as we find it given by nature. But what guarantees that this norm is a genuinely human norm? What possible answer could be given to this question so long as we do not know exactly what makes a person capable of studying or performing creative work? The future may teach us that these cases are just as "curable" as a cerebral tumor, although the term "curable" should then be understood in a new sense, viz., as governed by what in the future can become possible.

It is even difficult to imagine, we may add, that the norms which we now regard as natural norms will remain immutably valid in the future. This claim is not merely based on evolutionary considerations, which, of course, are difficult to harmonize with fixed natural conditions. The more specific reason becomes evident when one realizes the implications of the scientific question about the causes that give rise to the differences in character and intensity of human talents. From the standpoint of contemporary science man's intellectual grasp of, and operational grip on reality appear more and more to be conditioned by each other. For this reason a reply to the question about man's abilities implies, in principle, also the possibility that something can be done about them. Or, approaching the matter from the other side, if it appears that nothing can be done about them, our understanding of them must also be deficient. Yet a permanently deficient understanding can never be regarded as a human norm, at least not in the sense that we would be definitively resigned to it, for that would be the most flagrant violation of our freedom and intellectual aspirations.

Strictly speaking, nature itself does not impose any norms. Nature can imply a norm for us only insofar as we recognize nature as the inscrutable basis of our own existence. Nature in this sense, however, is never nature in its actual forms but always nature in its possibilities. It was a long time before physical science had progressed enough to stop regarding even external nature as something that was inviolably and immutably given. Man is still inclined to accept the natural distribution actually existing in human nature as an immutable starting point, with which he has to do the best he can. True, in the present state of affairs the human sciences cannot do anything else. They are restricted to investigating the possibilities existing within the context of the given conditions. Pedagogy and didactics, for example, investigate how education can best be adapted to the pupils' various levels of intelligence; but these levels themselves cannot at present be changed. However, we must ask, is the possibility of changing these levels absolutely excluded? Man never knows *a priori* how far his possibilities go, and this fact makes it all the more imperative that he explore them. But an essential condition of any such exploration is the above-mentioned "inner" break-through in physical science.

In this way we constantly come again to the conclusion that viewing human existence as freedom demands that we obtain more knowledge of man's material and vital structures as a truly active and conscious "spiritualization" of these structures. Only through this knowledge can man's freedom grow. Only through this knowledge does freedom get an opportunity to realize itself effectively as the meaningful freedom of a spirit-in-matter.

3. ETHICS AND PROGRESS

One of the arguments always brought to bear against any belief in progress is based on the fact that, no matter what has changed and will change, man remains essentially the same. This argument, we may add, is used equally against the humanistic belief in man himself and the Christian belief in man's inner conversion to God and His commandments. "What has been accomplished by two thousand years of Christianity?" so runs the argument in one case, and "What else have science and technology brought us but deathly dangers?" argues the other. Granted that there has been a measure of progress in some areas, can one say that there has been genuine progress in man's humanity, understood either in a Christian or a humanistic sense? Briefly put, has there been moral progress? Has man become better?

These questions, which were already asked in the introductory chapter, are not purely academic, especially now that non-Western cultures have begun to take over the achievements of the West in scientific, organizational and technical matters. For, in practice this take-over often means that those cultures lose their inner core. And, if that happens, what do they gain from taking over the achievements of the West? So long as the West considered its own culture to be generally superior to the others, it could hardly have seen a problem here. But the situation changed when the West began to doubt itself, for it realized that all its progress meant very little from the ethical standpoint.

The heart of the problem here lies in a peculiar characteristic of moral obligation, which we may call its "absoluteness." By referring to this absoluteness, we do not want to take sides in the famous dispute whether ethics can be absolute or merely relative, for that question is not immediately at stake here, even though it is true that it cannot be entirely eliminated. What we mean here by absoluteness is that the moral obligation is absolute, in the sense that it is obligatory in all conditions, regardless of whether or not the content of the moral obligation is subject to modifications. The concrete realization of the moral obligation can perhaps be quite different in different situations, but the obligation as obligation always holds, no matter what the conditions and the situation are. Only where there is no longer question of being-man does the moral obligation cease. In this sense the obligation has an absolute character.

Every situation confronts man with ethical norms, even if one accepts a variation in these norms. And, even this variation participates to some extent in the absoluteness of the moral obligation, insofar as the modifications of its ethical content are not arbitrary but somehow remain governed by general ethical principles. For these general principles, precisely because they are norms of the variations, themselves possess a certain absolute character in both of the above-mentioned senses. Thus it follows that, ethically speaking, the actually existing conditions are not indifferent. As soon as man discovers that *de facto* existing conditions can be modified in such a way that the general moral obligation can be better satisfied, it can become an ethical duty for man to change these conditions.

The ethical obligation is never something purely formal and, as it were, devoid of content, but always is concerned with the realization of a definite goal. To illustrate the matter, consider the moral demands contained in the idea of Christian charity. These demands evidently are valid under all conditions, in the former society that knew slavery and in contemporary society, in the former view of earthly reality that seemed to leave no room for effective Christian charity and in the contemporary view that envisions effectiveness.

So long as slavery seemed to be a natural condition and man seemed unable to change nature, the *abolition* of slavery could not be a moral obligation. But there existed an obligation to realize the ideal of charity to the best of one's ability within the framework of the relations arising from slavery. The same situation prevailed with respect to helping the sick and the poor. So long as illness and need are considered a "natural" part of human existence, there can be no moral obligation to eliminate them. But that obligation arises concomitantly with the possibility of eliminating them.

A peculiar problem arises in the context of these considerations; one can ask when the ideal of charity was most intensely pursued. In evaluating a period of time or a particular culture, what should be the norm: the way in which within the limited realm of possibilities people made a virtue of necessity or the way in which they tried to enlarge the existing possibilities? The fact that both parts of this question can receive different answers indicates that there is a certain ambivalence in the evaluation of the progress made in the West. For it is not at all evident in which period of history the spirit of Christian charity has been most inspiring: in ancient times with their slavery, in the Middle Ages with charitable care of the sick and the poor, or in our time in which the care of the sick and the poor has become an integral part of normal social services.

Regardless of the importance of the above-mentioned distinction and the resulting twofold question, the answer to the one has, nevertheless, to be considered separately from the other. Even if the ideal of charity in former times gave a more intense inspiration than it does now, this much remains certain: as soon as it became evident that slavery was not a "natural" condition, as soon as it became evident that man in need could be effectively assisted, the abolition of slavery and effective measures against human needs simply became an ethical obligation. If, in a comparison between the Middles Ages and our time, medieval man would be judged to have lived the ideal of Christian charity more intensely, this evaluation could never imply that we must give up our modern systems of caring for the sick and the poor, but only that the demand to be made of us now is to let the spirit of charity inspire our social services in the same way as it inspired medieval charitable works.[15]

It is true undoubtedly that the pursuit of science and technology themselves do not guarantee the spirit of charity. Nevertheless, once

---

[15]All this, however, does not imply that charitable works in the old senses of the term have no longer any value. Cf. van Melsen, "Technik und Caritas," *Das Krankenhaus,* vol. 54 (1962), pp. 410-417.

science and technology have been discovered, they become indispensable from the viewpoint of charity; hence man may and must develop them. There have been times when man's ethical obligations could be fulfilled independently of them, but for us that is evidently no longer the case. For contemporary man the development of science and technology is, from the moral standpoint, not optional but obligatory.

Strange as this may seem to some, there is an inner connection between morality and the pursuit of physical science. Yet, strictly speaking, is it not true that such a connection should be expected if we take into account that the original philosophical impulse continues to move physical science as well as all other sciences? As is generally known, in Greek philosophy, despite its orientation to disinterested knowledge, there was an intimate bond between this knowledge and ethics. The Greek concept of wisdom referred to an attitude of life which implied both intellectual understanding of the essence of things and a corresponding moral life.[16] Wisdom was based on the unity of *theoria* and *praxis*.

One special aspect of the bond between physical science and morality is that the development of this science in its possibilities for practical application opens up perspectives on ethical ideals which former generations could hardly even dream of; for instance, an existence worthy of man for everyone and effective means to combat illness, poverty and ignorance. For this reason technology considered as *praxis* participates in a special way in the ethical *praxis* connected with wisdom. Thus science appears to share not only in the cognitive aspect but also in the operational aspect of man's desire for wisdom from which Greek philosophy was born.

In the light of the preceding considerations it becomes possible to answer such worrisome questions as: Does all that progress also mean an increase in morality? Have men become better than they were? The reply is simply that morality itself demands this progress and that in a certain sense, therefore, the question itself is irrelevant.

There is more, however. In this chapter we are not only concerned with man's increasing control over external conditions but also, and especially, with a perspective on a possible control over internal conditions, a perspective on man's internal growth in freedom. But internal freedom and morality are most intimately con-

---

[16]Concerning this matter see C. J. de Vogel, "What Philosophy Meant to the Greeks," *International Philosophical Quarterly*, vol. 1 (1961), pp. 35-58.

nected. Without this freedom there can be no morality because morality always implies that one can place oneself at a distance from what *de facto* is, in order to see what it ought to be. If, then, internal freedom increases, morality receives a greater opportunity to realize what ought to be. Here, too, one can ask whether man will actually make use of this opportunity. Again, however, the answer will have to be that, no matter how important this question is, the possibility that man will fail to use it does not decide the issue whether or not there is a moral obligation to strive for greater freedom. This moral obligation has a priority and cannot be eliminated by any doubts about the possible uses man will make of this freedom.

4. THE EVALUATION OF DIFFERENT CULTURES

Guided by the insights of the preceding section, it becomes possible to find a satisfactory answer to the question whether the West has the right to share its achievements with other cultures when there is danger that these cultures will perish in the process. As in the comparison between earlier and later phases of Western culture itself, there is no question here of making a comparative evaluation of cultures in all their aspects but only of recognizing universal human values. While to demand that a culture be evaluated according to all its aspects rather than certain aspects comes close to being a sophism, this demand seems to be the only point that is ultimately of importance, and in a certain sense, as we will see presently, that is true. At the same time, however, it forces us to raise the problem in a very deceptive way, simply because it is beyond man to evaluate a culture totally and integrally. There are several reasons for this.

Man does not possess the power to encompass and to penetrate everything with an all-pervading glance. Our knowledge is abstract and partial, and therefore our norms can be only abstract and partial. For this reason our evaluation of cultures can never be more than partial. Secondly, man's way of knowing also implies that certain aspects of a culture lend themselves more easily to an evaluation than others. Finally, cultures are no longer static but dynamic. This point needs to be explicitated somewhat.

With respect to the past and the present of a culture, man is able to arrive at a partial survey of its many component elements, but with respect to the future such a survey is much more difficult. Yet the value of a culture depends not only on what it is now but also on its vitality for the future. For this reason the evaluation of existing cultures has to take into account also their power of assimilation and openness to new developments. For a human culture is not the same as a certain pattern of behavior among animals. An animal behavior pattern does not have to change as long as the external conditions to which it is adapted are not modified. If these conditions are changed, then the pattern has to be adapted to the new situation; but the question whether the conditions will change does not depend upon the animal. Man, on the other hand, has an inner desire to change the environment in which he happens to exist into his world, to control constantly more of it and to control it more perfectly. In this way man's "law of development" differs from that of an animal. Consequently, the dynamism of a culture belongs to its very essence, for this dynamism is not merely a reaction to "accidentally" changed conditions but one of the foundations of the culture as a human culture.

This dynamism also implies that every culture will endeavor to take over those elements of other cultures that have a universal value. In this sense the "level" of a culture is co-determined by its ability to recognize and assimilate universal values. But it is exceedingly difficult to determine *a priori* whether a particular culture is able to do so.

For the above-mentioned reasons it is not possible for man to make a total evaluation of a culture. This impossibility, however, does not mean that the desire for such an evaluation is entirely in vain. The sophism mentioned at the beginning of this section would not be a sophism if it did not contain a semblance of truth, and such a semblance can be based only on the fact that a grain of truth is contained in it. The grain of truth contained in man's desire to have a total evaluation of a culture manifests itself, first of all, in that in any evaluation of a culture we must realize that an aspect of a culture is *no more* than an aspect. Indirectly, therefore, the culture in its totality remains our point of orientation. Only one who realizes that the totality is more than this aspect can evaluate the aspect as an aspect.

Secondly, man devotes himself to the various aspects of a culture because of his interest in the culture's totality, for he knows that only in this way he is able to improve the totality. For this reason we develop science and technology although they are only partial values, and for this reason also we endeavor to eliminate their unfavorable repercussions upon the totality, such as the social consequences of the industrial revolution. There is no other way in which we can proceed in our development, for the partial character of our knowledge is of necessity shared by our action. Just as our cognitive grasp of things is necessarily one-sided, so also our technical grip on them. Neither our grasp nor our grip can encompass all aspects. This one-sidedness also explains why all social development implies dislocations: one can never foresee what the concrete, the total, results will be of a certain technical discovery or of a particular social innovation. Only *post factum* can these total results be known and corrected.[17]

Only by way of partial approaches does man's desire for the integrity of cultural totality assume a concrete form. In and through dissonant approaches we strive for harmony. This too is an aspect of the above-mentioned immanent "law of development." This development implies man's freedom and consequently also a developmental driving force residing in him. Yet it implies at the same time the deficiency of man's approach, manifesting itself in his one-sided handling of his problems and, last but not least, his purely relative "providence." Because our "providence" is so relative, it can be very instructive to make comparisons with earlier cultures and with different cultures, for such comparisons help us keep in mind the many aspects that are of importance. Accordingly, although a total comparison is not possible, a partial comparison can help us realize that we are deficient and where we fall short.

This realization, however, should not lead us to neglect the new possibilities that reveal themselves, especially since it has not been excluded that much of what we customarily ascribe unqualifiedly to a failure of man should really be attributed to his immaturity. For example, many things that were regarded as moral defects in the past were perhaps only manifestations of a lack of inner freedom. Man can sin only with full knowledge and full consent, so moralists tell us, and therefore a little child cannot sin. What, however, is an adult, a mature man?

5. Maturity as a Problem

Before man had learned to think "under the aspect of evolution," the question of what adulthood meant was easily answered. Every

[17] This unpredictability flows in part also from the experimental character of our knowledge. Concerning this matter, see van Melsen, *Science and Technology,* Chapter XV.

man underwent the same processes of growth and development, whose
limits were set by the unchangeable "species." With respect to man,
the term "species" was taken philosophically rather than biologically
but that did not take away from the fact that man's possibilities had
been fixed once and forever. The ethical norms were determined by
these possibilities. If in an ethical context there was question of a
mature man, his maturity and his corresponding freedom were judged
according to the norms indicated by human nature. If, however,
the static norms are no longer normative, if it is possible for man to
grow in freedom, then man's morality can likewise grow. Theo-
retically speaking, there is undoubtedly room for a growth of freedom, for man's freedom is often in a sad state. Much of what we
call man's sinfulness and wickedness is really based on the fact that
he is controlled by his passions, whose irresistibleness is largely to
be blamed on their relative autonomy.

Hitherto it was axiomatic that this autonomy was a fundamental
characteristic of human existence, which simply had to be accepted
as such. But, we may ask, is that really the case? Once more, the
question cannot be answered *a priori,* but it is certain that every
opportunity to overcome the situation must be used. The idea that
much of what was traditionally called sinfulness and wickedness is
essentially a matter of illness is now commonly accepted in the various human sciences, even though we do not yet possess effective
means of overcoming this illness. Our lack of knowledge here is
not surprising if we recall the extremely defective manner in which
we know the interconnection of the spheres of matter, life, and man.
As long as man does not possess this knowledge, can he be regarded
as really grown-up, mature?

It is interesting to note that Christian tradition has always realized that man was not what he really ought to be. This defect was
not attributed to man's lack of "maturity" but to the effects of original
sin, which obscured man's mind and weakened his will. The absence
of an evolutionary perspective practically compelled Christian tradition to consider this situation as a permanent feature of man's earthly
existence, one which was not even removed by Christ's redemption.
But, is it really true that this situation is permanently fixed? Cannot
these so-called darkness of mind and weakness of will be a reference
to human possibilities that are as yet unrealized or that have to be
realized again? The "inner" break-through in physical science is,
strictly speaking, nothing but a clearer self-presence and an intensi-

fication of freedom. For this reason, once again the idea imposes itself that this break-through may perhaps prove of decisive value not only for science but for the entire future of mankind, for mankind's growth to fullness, to maturity.

Encouraging as these considerations may be with respect to physical science's possible value for the inner growth of human freedom, they fail to include one aspect of perhaps, crucial importance. Man does not simply fall short in the fulfillment of what he regards as his moral obligation; much worse, mankind disagrees about the content of the moral obligations. We merely touched this point very briefly in mentioning the absolute character of the moral obligation; yet it is a matter of the greatest importance and has to be considered. However, we prefer to reflect upon this topic in a broader framework than mere ethics and to speak about it in connection with the lack of harmony in philosophy in general. For the divison of views on ethical matters is merely a symptom of this general disagreement in philosophical questions.

CHAPTER NINE

THE PROGRESS OF PHILOSOPHY

1. The Lack of Harmony in Philosophy

Perhaps no other sign indicates more eloquently the failure of man's self-consciousness than his inability, manifesting itself in the painfully divided state of philosophical thought, to sound the depth of his own being. This lack of harmony, however, is not something that finds expression only in philosophy itself, for otherwise one could perhaps regard that division as a matter of purely academic importance. As we have seen in the preceding chapters, this division extends also to the empirical human sciences. Their controversy about the proper method mirrors the division of philosophy concerning the view to be taken of man himself. The various schools of thought in the different human sciences are clearly connected with philosophical trends of thinking.

Only physical science seems to escape this philosophical divisiveness. This escape, however, is limited to the direct pursuit of physical science, for as soon as one asks about the meaning of this pursuit, the situation changes to reveal the full consequences of the philosophical lack of harmony. These consequences are not restricted to the relatively narrow circles of people with professional interest in philosophical matters. For the fact of such an ambivalent attitude toward the value of physical science constitutes one of the most important causes of the crisis faced by Western culture. The reason is that the influence of physical science and its applications reaches all aspects of life, whether cultural or social.

In this way the divisiveness of philosophy extends to all regions, including the realm of action. The clearest sign that even the realm of action is affected by philosophy's division is perhaps that mankind not only falls short of what is morally seen to be good but also disagrees about what should be regarded as ethically good.

Nevertheless, as we have pointed out in the preceding chapters, it would be wrong to evaluate the lack of harmony in philosophy only in a negative way. The division of philosophy also has a positive side, in the sense that it indicates man's realization of how far he

186

remains from the goal, from the possession of the truth, so that he restlessly continues to push onward. While a particular philosopher or a particular school of philosophy may sometimes think that it has a monopoly on the truth, mankind in general has never been misled by such claims. In every instance, other thinkers relentlessly disclose the limitations of any such attempt to grasp *the* truth. And, what is even more interesting, mankind has never permanently resigned itself to philosophical confessions that the truth cannot be attained. Even the philosophical declarations that all knowledge is merely relative impress man as being too absolute.

This peculiar situation can be understood to some extent if attention is paid to the tension between the real limitation of human knowledge and man's awareness of this limitation, which is the great mystery of human existence itself. By his awareness of the limitation man transcends it. He knows through his transcendence that he is oriented to the totality of being, and for this reason he never gives up but constantly renews his attempt to grasp this totality. At the same time, however, his limitation makes it impossible for him to attain the desired goal. The primordial tension resulting from this situation also explains why man can never resign himself to any ultimate declaration, be it a philosophical system that wants to fixed once and for all the limits of what man can attain (Kantianism) or a philosophical view that claims to have gotten definitively rid of philosophy (positivism).

A positive evaluation of philosophical divisiveness, however, requires an effort to penetrate beyond the simple statement that the lack of harmony proves how much man realizes the limitation of any attempt to encompass the totality of being. This realization itself contains a dynamic element which animates not only philosophy but the whole of human existence in all its activities. For man's existence **is transcendental openness**, it is in its totality a question. For this reason, not only the history of philosophy, but the entire history of mankind is a constantly renewed question.

In Chapter Six we pointed out how man's philosophical question regarding his own being underlies all questions of the different sciences and how, therefore, this question becomes spatialized in the side-by-side existence of the multiple sciences and temporalized in their development. Understandably, then, the answer to the philosophical question cannot be given independently of these sciences and their development and especially not when their influence on human history is disregarded. Since, moreover, the philosophical question is a total question, it follows that no answer can ever be complete unless man first becomes the man he should be. But man cannot become the man he should be without first knowing about that man, and he cannot really know what he should be unless he brings his own potentialities to realization. Hence philosophy is never more than a being "on the way," for man himself is always "on the way." This being "on the way," however, is of necessity a going forward along *many* roads at the same time, roads that are many both in philosophy and in science.

2. Specialiazation in Science and the Divisiveness of Philosophy

Man is not exactly pleased with the many separate sciences and their ever increasing specialization. Nevertheless, he is, at least provisionally, willing to accept this situation as a consequence of the abstract character of human knowledge, which forces him to make use of many different methodic approaches. However, in the case of philosophy, he does not want to resign himself to the existing division, which he regards as a disgrace, attributable probably to the impatience or the obstinacy of the philosophers. Yet there is an intimate connection between the plurality of the sciences and the plurality of philosophies, for the latter reflects the former in a certain respect.

To understand this connection we must first see how the philosophical question becomes differentiated in the many sciences. The peculiar point about this differentiation is that there remains something of the original universality. Strange as it may seem, almost every science has a tendency to look on itself as the universal science. One of the many forms in which this tendency manifests itself is that the method proper to one's own science is considered to be *the* method, in comparison with which the methods of the other sciences are more or less provisional and destined to be replaced in due time by the privileged, universal method. This tendency is rather general among people devoting themselves to physical science; we may even say that physical science is congenitally infected by it. For when this science arose in the seventeenth century, it regarded itself as the lawful heir of medieval philosophy, which, in spite of its own division, seemed to possess a kind of universality in its method, more universality at least than appeared possible in later times.

Similar absolutizing tendencies with respect to method can be found in the importance some people attach to the application of mathematics in human sciences, like psychology, sociology and economics. They regard the mathematical method as ultimately the only valid method, just as others swear by the phenomenological method. To name a few other familiar examples, are not the tendencies to reduce psychology to biology and history to economics clear indications of the existence of such absolutizing trends? And if a reduction proves impossible, there is always the possibility of dismissing the other science as trivial or devoid of interest and regarding one's own type of science as the only one that really matters. The philosopher especially is exposed to this temptation, but he is certainly not the only one who falls for it.

We do not want to claim that all these tendencies to universalize one's own method are signs of wisdom. Yet they should not be dismissed as mere manifestations of narrow-mindedness, for it is true that every method and every science possesses essentially something universal. For instance, there is no realm in which physical science can find no application, no realm in which mathematics cannot clarify anything, and no realm either in which the science of language is devoid of importance. Likewise, anyone who has become attentive to the historical dimension of man will be unable to deny history its universality.

The classical formula which best expresses this situation is that the sciences are characterized by a difference in their formal object rather than their material object. Contemporary philosophers would probably prefer to say that every science thematizes the whole of reality in a certain way: the "attitude" (*Einstellung* in Husserl's terms) of the knowing subject makes reality appear in a certain light.[1] Regardless of the way in which the matter is expressed, it always implies that any concrete reality can in some respect be the object of any science. Stars and neuroses are, be it in different ways, objects of physical science and sciences of law, of theology and history, of sciences of language and literary critique, of psychology and economics, of chemistry and biology, and, of course, also of astronomy and medical science.

Accordingly, every science has something universal but, nevertheless, these many universalities, taken together, do not constitute universal knowledge of reality. They are too distinct and too different from

---

[1] Cf. Joseph J. Kockelmans, *Phenomenology and Physical Science,* Chapters 1-4 (to be published by Duquesne University Press).

one another to be simply merged into a single whole. Thus the temptation arises to assign philosophy the task of discerning in the universalities of the different sciences the specific contribution each can make to universal knowledge. For, is not philosophy the universal science *par excellence?* And does not philosophy explicitate the implicit answers to philosophical questions contained in the various sciences? Philosophy, then, so the conclusion goes, must be able to grasp the partial wisdoms of the sciences in a synthetizing grasp and to integrate them in one all-encompassing, all-pervading wisdom. Yet one who expects this of philosophy will have his hopes disappointed: the philosophers will inevitably fall short of his expectations because such an integration would transcend man's limited cognitive possibilities. If that integration were possible there would be no need for a plurality of sciences.

However, even if the integration is not possible, one might insist, why must philosophy be so divided? It could achieve harmony by limiting itself to showing why man's tendency to all-embracing knowledge can be realized only in defeat, in the dispersed character of many partial wisdoms. Philosophy should abandon its claim to attain reality by means of aprioristic deductions, which lead to such divergent results. It should restrict itself to a much more humble task, as is done by some forms of philosophy. We may reply that these forms of philosophy which want to restrict it to more humble tasks themselves disagree about what these tasks are to be. In other words, the division remains, whether philosophy wants to be humble or not, or even whether it wants to eliminate itself or not. This lack of harmony appears to be the pernicious effect of a kind of metaphysical "original sin." One wonders whether the aspirations of philosophy and their resulting division would not have been kept more under control if man's rise to scientific knowledge had not started with metaphysics.

How intimate the relation is between the accepted plurality of the sciences and the rejected divisiveness of philosophy is not difficult to see. For the above-mentioned claim to universality of the various sciences is not a purely scientific thesis but consciously or unwittingly a *philosophical* evaluation of the method proper to the science in question. As a matter of fact, the many divergent philosophical trends are all connected with faith in the universality of a particular methodic approach.

A few examples may illustrate this assertion. Descartes' rationalism believed in the universal validity of the mathematical method and empiricism clung to the empirical method proper to physical science. Kant's philosophy also arose from the conviction that the method of physical science had a universal and, in a sense, even exclusive value; and he tried to connect the rational and empirical aspects of this method. The same condition prevails today. Phenomenology, for example, regards the phenomenological method as *the* method, not only for the positive human sciences for which Husserl first devised this method, but also for philosophy. Proponents of linguistic analysis feel that the analysis of language is *the* philosophical method, logicians universalize the mathematico-logical method, metaphysicians continue to believe in the classical method of philosophy as *the* method, and dialecticians preserve faith in dialectics.

Additional differences could, of course, be added to the one stressed above,[2] but the tendency to universalize a particular method is especially illuminating. Here also it remains incorrect to evaluate the lack of harmony in philosophy in a purely negative way, for all those methods do possess a universal value not only in science but also in philosophy.

3. Perennial Philosophy

Human knowledge is limited, and this limitation expresses itself in the plurality of the sciences and the division existing in philosophy. On the other hand, man's knowledge is also infinitely open, as is shown by both science and philosophy's dynamic restlessness based on man's awareness that the limitation of his knowledge is a limitation. Once we realize the inner tension between that limitation and that openness, it is not difficult to recognize a kind of perennial philosophy in the manifold of different philosophies. The genuine unity and self-consistency expressed by the term "perennial philosophy" becomes discernible in various ways through and in spite of all divisiveness and historical development of philosophy. We will consider these ways in the following pages.

As we have repeatedly emphasized, man's philosophical questioning continues in science. In Chapter Two especially we have tried to ex-

---

[2] It would be interesting, for example, to distinguish the various trends in philosophy on the basis of the way in which they explain man's evident failure to attain the philosophical ideal.

plain how this continuation should be understood. It does not mean that science is the same as philosophy, but that the method of physical science contains a certain view of nature and of man as the subject of science. For this reason the unity and fixed character of this method unmistakably embodies a perennial philosophy. This perennial philosophy is continually re-affirmed by the confidence in the method of physical science with which the man of science pursues his studies and with which mankind applies the result of his studies.

These remarks apply not only to physical science but to a certain extent also to all other sciences. In its approach to reality any science is guided by a certain implicit view of this reality, a kind of perennial philosophy. If certain sciences, such as the human sciences, have not yet clearly established their method, this controversy about method should not make us forget the many common elements uniting all those who pursue the human sciences. Their arguments concerning method do not contradict these common elements, but merely affirm that further development is needed to solve the obscurity surrounding their unsolved methodological problems.

Our example of biology may again be used to clarify the matter. The controversy between vitalism and mechanism was also a dispute about method. This controversy arose from a twofold vision regarding the object of biology, one which stressed that the living organism certainly was a material structure, and another emphasizing that life had a specific character of its own. At first these two views seemed to clash; but the history of biology has clarified the issue, especially with respect to method. In contemporary biology the mechanism versus vitalism dispute hardly continues to play a role, at least its influence no longer blocks progress. From the methodic standpoint, biology has found the road which it should follow.

The fact that a science has found a firm method, however, does not necessitate unanimity regarding the philosophical explicitation of the implicit philosophical views contained in the method. The vigorous philosophical discussions around physical science clearly show how much divergence there can be. Thus it could seem that in order to speak of a perennial philosophy here the term would have to be restricted to that which remains implicit. But such a restriction would reduce that philosophy to the implicit, which does not appear to be very philosophical. For, is it not true that philosophy begins to be philosophy only on the reflective level? Although this question may be answered in the affirmative, it does not force us automatically to abandon the idea of a perennial philosophy. For this philosophy manifests itself also in other ways, which it is now time to consider.

Alfred N. Whitehead has remarked somewhere that the entire philosophy of the West can be regarded as a series of footnotes to Plato. One need not be a Platonist to agree fundamentally with this view; the high regard in which Greek philosophy continues to be held among philosophers confirms Whitehead's idea. Far from being limited to professional historians, anyone who wants to delve deeply into contemporary philosophy would be greatly handicapped if he were to keep aloof from ancient Greek thought.[3]

The same, however, cannot be affirmed with respect to other branches of knowledge. While almost all sciences are rooted in Greek thought, their concrete pursuit does not demand that one start with the ancient Greeks. A contemporary can be an excellent physicist, chemist, biologist, mathematician, astronomer, physician, psychologist or sociologist without being familiar with what Archimedes, Democritus, Aristotle, Euclid, Ptolemy, Hippocrates, Socrates or Plato have said about the sciences in question. This statement does not imply, of course, that such a familiarity is unimportant, for the relationship existing between philosophy and science clearly shows the opposite. Anyone reflecting upon his science is wittingly or unwittingly in contact with Greek thought. But the reading of Archimedes or Democritus contributes nothing to clarify the problems faced in modern nuclear research, and Hippocrates is not exactly illuminating when one wants to make progress in cancer research.

On the other hand, for one who is confronted with problems of philosophy of nature arising from the recent development of physics, the reading of Aristotle, Plato or Democritus can be very fruitful.[4] Likewise, the controversy between mechanism and vitalism in biology, as we have noted in Chapter Five, leads us back to Aristotle and Democritus. So also one who investigates the foundations of mathematics will be surprised to see that Plato has become his interlocutor. In medical science the psychosomatic problems lead to fundamental anthropological issues, in which Plato again appears on the scene. And in this way one can continue. The preceding examples are not a few very carefully selected topics that happen to

---

[3]For this point see also J. Moreau, *La conscience et l'être*, Paris, 1958.
[4]Cf. van Melsen, *From Atomos to Atom. The History of the Concept "Atom,"* Pittsburgh, 1952, Chapter VII.

have a certain affinity with ancient Greek problems, but all these problems, which get full attention in man's reflection upon the contemporary condition of particular sciences, refer to fundamental issues.

While it is true that today thinkers agree as little about these problems as did the ancient Greeks, at least the problems as such belong to perennial philosophy and must be considered as perennial philosophical problems. To think that psychosomatic problematics could arise only in modern medicine as a result of its contemporary development would be to misjudge this problematics in its inmost essence. True, the development of science obviously plays a role in the way in which the problems are raised; but for a good understanding of this role, it is necessary to realize that the problem in question is itself a fundamental philosophical problem which is much older than modern medical science.

Similar remarks apply to the other examples mentioned above. To understand the philosophical importance of Einstein's and Bohr's discussions precipitated by quantum mechanics, it is necessary to see behind them the age-old opposition between Plato and Aristotle. A correct perspective upon contemporary problems of philosophy, therefore, requires that attention be paid to Greek philosophy and, for that matter, to the *entire* history of philosophy. Whether or not one thinks that Whitehead honors Plato too much by relating the whole of history to this ancient sage does not matter very much, for the history of philosophy in any case is a continuous discussion of the perennial philosophy raised by the Greeks. For this reason even those thinkers who do not favor Plato very much remain in discussion with him. Plato cannot be disposed of once and for all in the same way as chemistry has disposed of the phlogiston theory or the theory of four elements.

The fact that the philosophical problematics retains its actuality, however, does not exclude new developments, for this problematics is continued in the various sciences and these sciences undergo development. In addition, the sciences develop within the framework of their methodic approach to reality and certain perennial philosophical views are embodied in this approach. Thus whatever development there is remains within the horizon open to these views; the new philosophical elements that manifest themselves remain within the original realm of discussion pertaining to perennial philosophy.

This statement applies especially to the topic of this book, the idea of evolution. In one sense this idea is new, namely, insofar as evolution in its biological sense proposed the descent of life and of man from inorganic matter and in its historical sense conceived mankind and its activities as characterized by progressiveness. Yet, in spite of its newness, the idea of evolution was a continuation of age-old problems. Although even in antiquity there existed a variety of more or less vague evolutionary ideas, more important is that the theory of biological descent fits into the general framework of the "scale of nature" and therefore merely raises in a new way the ancient problem of the inner relationship of all beings.

Likewise, the idea of progressiveness may be termed new, but nonetheless it fitted in with Greek awareness of history, for the ancient Greek thinkers strongly realized that philosophy had gone through a period of development in their time. What was new was that, since the rise of physical science as a progressive science, the idea of progressive development had to be extended also to the future. The discussions of the preceding chapter regarding the question whether one may speak of total human development and the hesitation of many to give an affirmative answer to this question show that the Greeks touched the heart of the question when they assigned a "ceiling" to human development. Christian eschatology, we may add, likewise indicates that the idea of evolution as a historical category did not land in an intellectual vacuum but in a familiar climate.

Meanwhile perennial philosophy is not only an everlasting discussion of the same fundamental themes. Through the divergence of the answers one can discern a development which excludes certain replies given in former times or at least makes them less probable.

Hegel saw the history of philosophy as a development in which a thesis would call for an antithesis, both of which would then merge into a synthesis. This synthesis in its turn would function as a new thesis needing an antithesis to reach a new synthesis on a higher level, and so on, without, however, ever reaching the terminus of the mind's ascending movement. Hegel's idea is a fascinating proposal and can explain many things in history, especially when it is conceived in a broad way so as to include man's non-philosophical activities in philosophy's own dialectic development. For, if the philosophical question is continued in science, there exists also a dialectics of science and philosophy; just as within the framework of non-philosophical activities there is also a dialectics of scientific theory and practice.

Thus the objection against Hegel's view is not so much that it is false as that it takes too few dimensions of man's thinking into account. In reality, the development of thought covers simultaneously many dimensions, and so many of its aspects cross and intercross that it becomes difficult to discern the dialectic lines of development. Moreover, Hegel thought it sufficient to survey the past while modern man realizes that he should look first and foremost to the future.

Although Hegel's idea was too schematic,[5] it had the great merit of showing that the recurrence of dialectic oppositions on a new level is not a mere repetition but implies also a permanent gain. For example, as we have seen in Chapter Seven, the manner in which the new era raised the problem of causality and finality was, on the one hand, a definitive gain but, on the other, a loss with respect to the old view because the problem was put in a one-sided and narrow fashion. However, the development of physical science has forced the philosopher to correct this one-sidedness. Elements of the old view have regained importance, even though there is no question of simply and fully returning to the ancient view. If, for instance, finality plays again a more important role in our world view than was ascribed to it in that of the new era, this increased importance does not at all mean that finality is restored to its original position in the ancient or medieval world view.

Accordingly, there is a development and this may be called a dialectic development, for the original insights continue to exist in a more profound and refined way. Yet it does not follow that we are able to objectivize this development fully and clearly distinguish the perennial elements present in the past from other transient, elements. Such a distinction obviously could be made only if the process of development had reached its term. As long as this is not the case there is always a danger of discrepancy between the implicit tendencies of the development and their philosophical explicitation. In the preceding chapters we have seen many examples of that discrepancy. Chapter Three showed that the implicit view of material reality embodied in the method of physical science was much richer than its explicitation by the philosophy of the new era. And Chapter Seven revealed the same with respect to the question of causality and finality. Only after developments have run their course is it

---

[5]For Hegel also it was true that non-philosophical considerations played an important role in his thinking. Cf. Alphonse de Waelhens, *La philosophie et les expériences naturelles,* The Hague, 1961, pp. 1-41.

possible to explicitate their value with a measure of accuracy. In this sense philosophical reflection always has to lag behind actual developments, no matter how much it stimulates them in other respects.

Even taking into account that philosophy has to lag behind in the above-mentioned sense and therefore can speak about recent development only with much circumspection, would not eliminate the difficulties. For it is evident that the lack of harmony in philosophy also plays a role in the philosophical explicitation and evaluation of elements which are clearly revealed by the development of human thought. A positivist does not evaluate in the same way as a phenomenologist. Only if there were no longer any division in philosophy or if that division were no longer important, would it be possible for all philosophers to attribute the same value to the developments that have taken place. For any sifting of valuable from the non-valuable elements contained in the past and in the present can be made only on the basis of absolutizing a particular "superphilosophy" as a system or as a guiding idea. And in comparison with this all other views must then be regarded as philosophical heresies or at most as partial truths. But which thinker, with any historical awareness, would dare to say now that he is in possession of such a "superphilosophy"?

While a negative reply to this question would seem called for, can we say that this is the reply actually given? It appears that the singular fate of philosophy is to give an answer which somehow moves in the direction of a "superphilosophy" since the philosopher cannot escape from judging his own and all other philosophies from a "superstandpoint." There is no presumption involved in this but simply self-knowledge. This fate arises from the aspect of absoluteness that is unavoidably present in human knowledge, even if this aspect consists merely in man's awareness of the limitation of his knowledge. By virtue of philosophy's own nature, this aspect of absoluteness has to be present; and for this reason it is a typical characteristic of perennial philosophy. Nor is this characteristic merely formal; it is found in the most relativistic trends of philosophy just as well as in the most absolutistic trends. We may even say that it is more troublesome in the former because these pretend to have given up all absolutistic aspirations and thus add hypocrisy to their absoluteness.

Nevertheless, if it is true that philosophy finds its starting point in the equiprimordial givenness of human knowledge as relative and man's awareness of this relativity, then it must be possible to arrive at a fundamental philosophical attitude corresponding to this equi-primordial datum. Such an attitude, while rejecting any absolute relativism, must also evaluate every philosophical tradition as a courageous, though perhaps exaggerated, attempt to bring order into the plurality of data by starting with a certain central reference point. Without such an attempt no philosophy is possible and, more important, without it no advantage can be taken from the developments that have occurred in science and in reality. It is worth while noting that something like this attitude of mind is beginning to manifest itself in contemporary philosophy. Despite all the diverse currents and trends of thinking, a kind of dialogue is beginning to develop, not in a perfunctory way, but in all seriousness.

But such a dialogue is possible only in the belief that there exists a perennial philosophy in which a meeting of minds can occur in spite of all differences, one in which the diversity of answers and even of questions does not exclude an awareness that all are attempts to express and answer the same primordial philosophical question, viz., the question which man himself is. This awareness can undoubtedly find a strong support in the thought that the "failure" of philosophy, as it finds expression in the division of minds, should not be attributed to a failure of man as such, but results from the fact that man is not yet the man he should be.

If man, as we know him now, had reached the end of his possibilities, then his philosophical failure to achieve clarity about himself would indeed be a disgrace, and one could understandably expect that attempts would be made to camouflage this failure with an over-compensation of absoluteness in one form or in another. But if man is merely "on the way," is only in an incipient way the man he can and should be, then also philosophy can merely be philosophy in an incipient way. However, even this incipient philosophy belongs to perennial philosophy because it is an expression of the *man* who is "on the way," and not of a being that still has to become a man. As being "on the way," man contains the philosophical question in his very essence; we may even say that he *is* this question. In the progressive unfolding of his being through the sciences and their application in the building of his human world, man brings his own being to realization and at the same time fulfills the necessary condition for a better and more mature "understanding of being."

EPILOGUE

There exist two strikingly opposed standpoints with respect to the philosophical value of physical science. According to positivism, physical science now fills the role formerly played by philosophy. For it, philosophy is nothing but the incipient stage of science. In the positivistic view philosophy has had no specific function to fulfill since the rise of science, at least not with respect to man's knowledge of *reality*. Whatever value philosophy still retains lies entirely in a linguistic, methodic or logical analysis of the way science investigates and describes reality. As a metascientific[1] approach to reality, philosophy is an anachronism, a kind of living fossil which somehow survived instead of becoming extinct when the era of intellectual life to which it belonged came to an end.

Most trends of thought which hold that philosophy is important for man's knowledge of reality attribute a more modest position to physical science than does positivism. In their view, physical science undoubtedly reaches reality but only in an abstract and artificial fashion; philosophy, on the other hand, endeavors to attain reality in its primordial concreteness.

In this book we arrived at the conclusion that the thesis that philosophy studies reality in a more primordial fashion than physical science is not incompatible with the thesis that physical science occupies a definite key position in such a way that, to some extent, all progress depends upon that of this science. The assertion that these two theses are in harmony does not equate philosophy with physical science nor does it eliminate the distinction between physical sciences and human sciences. But the assertion does imply that man's primordial philosophical questioning is continued in all sciences, even in apparently aphilosophical physical science. The method of this science, the way in which physical science investigates reality, embodies an implicit view of reality, of man as the knower of this reality, and of their mutual relationship. This implicit vision grows richer and more profound as science progresses, but its enrichment remains as implicit as the vision itself. The explicitation of this vision occurs only in philosophical reflection. Because of the key position occupied by physical science, philosophical reflection upon

---

[1] We use this term here as having a broader sense than "metaphysical."

199

developments is not just one of the many branches of philosophy, but one of the most important philosophical disciplines. It is concerned with matters whose consequences are far beyond what one might expect from the sole consideration of the direct object proper to physical science.

Numerous examples have shown the truth of these assertions. The development of physical science has not only given us a more profound concept of nature and of matter, but man has also begun to regard himself in a different way, both with respect to his status of being as a spirit-in-matter and in regard to his cognitive and operational possibilities. Causality and finality were selected as examples, as was the relationship between theory and practice. The central point of our concern, however, was the investigation of the philosophical implications contained in the theory of evolution, primarily as a biological theory but also as a historical doctrine. Moreover, these implications showed themselves so important that they were able to modify our vision of philosophy itself. We will return to this point after adding a few more remarks about the key position of physical science in the entire process.

As the Introduction mentioned, there is much to suggest that the cosmic and biological evolution of nature, which culminated in the appearance of man, is continued in a human evolution in which the *science* of nature takes over the role formerly played by nature itself. Even after closer scrutiny this idea remains attractive. It contains much truth, but this truth does not imply that man must be merely a "physical animal" and not also a "metaphysical animal." Such an assertion would contradict the fact that physical science itself arose from philosophy, that is, the fact that man's first breakthrough, which freed him from a cosmic bond that encompassed both nature and man, was of a philosophical nature. On the other hand, it could very well be true that man will be able to develop his philosophical activities fruitfully only if he humbly accepts the fact that he is a "physical animal." We use this ambiguous term here intentionally to express the conviction that man's physical nature and his pursuit of physical science are intimately connected. Could not the fact that man is an "animal" in the biological sense imply that, in order to become more a man and a better man, he must above all study nature and especially biological nature?

This is not to say that physical science is man's most important and most noble pursuit, but it could mean that the pursuit of this science would be the most fundamental of all. In calling physical science "most fundamental," we do not merely refer to the old saying that life should come first and philosophy only after it. While undoubtedly this saying is true, one of the greatest misconceptions of our time is that physical science is generally regarded only from this standpoint, it is valued only as a means to raise man's material standard of living. If man is primarily a "physical animal," then the principal function of physical science must perhaps be sought in the perspectives it opens for raising man's spiritual standard of life.

In the preceding chapters we have seen many arguments pointing in this direction. They made clear how, from a long range standpoint, the original philosophical intuition which guides physical science in its methodic approach to reality, was purer in truth and more fruitful in possibilities of development than the philosophical reflections in which the philosophers of the past have tried to explicitate this original intuition. This fact is not a mere coincidence but indicates that the implicit way of philosophizing contained in the pursuit of physical science is one of the most important, perhaps even the only, way in which progress in philosophy is possible. We do not mean that physical science itself brings about this progress as *philosophical* progress, for only philosophical explicitation can accomplish that. However, the philosophical explicitation will have to be conscious of its dependence on physical science and consequently also of the typical limitation implied in this dependence.

Before philosophy became accustomed to the idea of progressive and experimental knowledge through the development of physical science, philosophy could be convinced that its explicitations had to be definitive and decisive. The first lesson it had to learn from physical science was patience. Its lack of patience also explains why past philosophy has so often wrongly evaluated the genuine implications of scientific development. Despite all its limitations and its awareness of them, philosophy thought itself obliged to pronounce a definitive judgment. Unsurprisingly, therefore, its judgments were often too hasty and too immature.

Of course, it is true that, so long as reality and man himself were conceived in a static way, there was little reason to assume an attitude of waiting. For, what sense could it make to wait? Man was what he was and reality was what it was. Thus the lack of harmony in philosophy was truly a disgrace, and the absoluteness with which philosophical positions were defended was the resulting overcompensation. Since then, as we have pointed out, physical science has demonstrated that human knowledge has a progressive character and has discovered that man himself forms part of the evolutionary progress. Consequently, now the division existing in philosophy appears in a new light. It appears probable now that man is not yet able to solve his fundamental problems because he is not yet the man he should be. In this way philosophical division becomes a sign of the openness of the human spirit, which refuses to abide permanently and generally by philosophical arguments based upon insufficient information about reality and about man himself.

If this line of thought is correct, then the value of physical science for philosophy is evident. This science is the means for increasing the necessary information, not so much about existing reality, as about what this reality can become under man's guidance and also about what man himself can become. The fact that all sciences are important in this respect does not contradict the thesis that physical science occupies the key position in this matter. This science holds the key with respect to man's knowledge of external reality; it holds the key also, be it in a different way, in regard to man's self-knowledge. Man's growing self-presence and freedom are conditioned by a better understanding of his own material structure.

A variety of consequences flow from the fact that physical science occupies this key position. Physical science is an experimental science, and the entire realm of reality that it directly or indirectly covers is influenced by this experimental character. We never know exactly beforehand whither certain developments originating from physical science will lead. This ignorance indicates that something of the unconscious and non-reflective character proper to prehuman evolution remains discernible even in evolution brought about by man. Man sees certain possibilities of development and endeavors to bring them to realization, but he is not able to foresee all their consequences. For this reason also much of what we have said in this book, of the things that have been proposed as philosophical theses, remain infected with uncertainty. Certainty about these matters can be obtained only when they have been realized.

Nevertheless, it remains worthwhile to reflect upon the future of mankind and of philosophy in the light of those theses. It is even necessary to do so, for man must think ahead and constantly distance himself from the concrete situation if he wants to have at least a measure of understanding of the possibilities implied in unexpected developments and make them his own as *human* possibilities. The same applies to philosophy and perhaps even especially to philosophy. Hence the fact that the theses put forward in this book remain infected with uncertainties does not destroy their value. We may add that this uncertainty alone does not render them inferior to theses proposed by the style of philosophizing proper to the past, which pretended to know everything exactly. Despite their margin of uncertainty the theses defended in this study offer a greater fundamental certainty. Although they are groping extrapolations, they are at least extrapolations of ideas that have already become certain.

Accordingly, in all the intellectual activity forced upon us by the pursuit of physical science and its application in other sciences and in many realms of reality, it is always necessary to remain expectantly open to the future experience of reality. This future experience, however, is never concerned with something so entirely new that it would in no way fit in with man's picture of reality. Otherwise it would contradict man's fundamental openness, expressing itself in the question he asks about being as being. For one who regards this argument as too metaphysical, past experience should provide a plausible proof. Whatever new developments have occurred, man has always been able to place them within the reach of what we have called "perennial philosophy." If, then, the margin of uncertainty seems to have increased, this increase is only apparent, at least in an absolute sense. Uncertainty has become greater and could become greater because our certainty also has grown. We think this certainty includes the idea that man, measured in cosmic terms, is still very young and that science and philosophy, measured in terms of what remains unknown, are likewise very young. This idea we may regard as the decisive perspective which the evolutionary theory has opened to philosophy.

INDEX OF NAMES

INDEX OF SUBJECT MATTER